What others are saying about

"A wild ride! Just when you thought you knew where it was going, it takes you to another level."

— Solon Tsangaras, Author, *Detour to Armageddon*

"The Girls of October is just plain genius. And it's so unorthodox that initially, we don't know what we're getting into. But 50 pages in you'll realize that this is more than just a unique piece, it's also a supremely wrapped gift to the horror fans of the world."

—*Horror Novel Reviews*

"Josh Hancock's novel reads like a true-crime book inspired by the John Carpenter film *Halloween.* I was completely sucked into this incredibly realistic horror story."

—Zakary McGaha, Author, *Sea of Medium-to-High Pitched Noises*

"The Girls of October is an engrossing read from beginning to end that's sure to entertain even the most desensitized horror fans."

—*Rue Morgue Magazine*

"As the pages turn, the movie reel inside the mind cranks with suspenseful intensity, contemplating what horrors will come to pass in the next scene of pure terror. Hancock delivers what true horror fans have been ravenous for and provides a new nightmare vision on every page with a uniquely genius storytelling template... "

—David J. Fairhead, Author, *The Fall Of Tomorrow, Dwelling In The Dark* and the voice and talent behind *Kettle Whistle Radio* Podcast

"For fans of horror fiction, especially horror films from the 1970s through the mid-1980s, this is required reading."

—*Haddonfield Horror*

"This is one of the most detailed horror books I've ever read. It is written in such a realistic manner, with quotes from various textbooks and news sources, it's almost hard to believe it's a work of fiction. Carefully crafted, each page draws in the reader like whispered secrets in one's ear."

—*Haunted San Diego*

What others are saying about *The Devil and My Daughter*:

"Fans of horror cinema and genuine inventiveness are in store for an exceptional read with some captivating characters and – as one might expect – some heartbreaking twists."

—*Horror Novel Reviews*

Other books by Josh Hancock:

The Girls of October

The Devil and My Daughter

Death Rituals

JOSH HANCOCK

Burning Bulb
PUBLISHING

Death Rituals
By **Josh Hancock**

Burning Bulb Publishing
P.O. Box 4721
Bridgeport, WV 26330-4721
United States of America
www.BurningBulbPublishing.com

Cover designed by Gary Lee Vincent and Josh Hancock with licensed images from iStockphoto LP.

First Edition.

Paperback Edition ISBN: 978-0997773071

Printed in the United States of America

Acknowledgments

Special thanks to Esha Krishnamoorthy, who created all of the promotional material and photographs for *Death Rituals*; Gary Vincent and Burning Bulb Publishing, whose unwavering support is second to none; and my wife, as always, for everything.

"The power to kill can be just as satisfying as the power to create."

—*Rope* (1948)

"A terrifying depiction of the most shocking news story in recent memory, this televised docudrama is essential viewing for anyone interested in true crime. The online bonus materials, compiled with the approval of the Alvarez family, provide a fascinating, man-behind-the-curtain study of a single night of horror." —*Entertainment Spotlight*

"Although this 90-minute TV movie grovels in its lurid subject matter, the result is an engrossing portrait of a horrific home invasion. If you're going to watch *The Apple Hill Murders*, keep the viewer's guide close at hand. From news articles to press releases, from interviews to essays and online message boards, these documents reveal the heart behind the tragedy: 21-year-old Cherie Alvarez, whose courage humbles all of us." —*TV Matters*

"Broadcast on a station known for tawdry, tabloid-style programming, *The Apple Hill Murders* is a surprisingly gripping experience, bursting with topical issues and grim social commentary. Viewers are encouraged to get involved in the broadcast by exploring a vast number of web materials—everything from archived news articles to a script of the teleplay itself. Told effectively, this is a true-life story with devastating implications." —*The Daily Review*

"Chilling and informative, *The Apple Hill Murders* shows little restraint in depicting the naked fury of Bobby Pruitt and his cult of brainwashed jailbird thugs. Rising above the blood-soaked fray are the three heroines of the story—Cherie, Coral, and Paula—who embody strength and justice in nearly every sequence of the film." —*Los Angeles Digital*

"Rather than present a wholly fictionalized account of the bloodbath that occurred in the foothills of Northern California, producer Brant Kulchner and writer Prairie Williams combine a gritty documentary style with the polished reenactments of true crime procedurals. Sure, the title is a bit of a misnomer (*The Apple Hill Justifiable Homicides* doesn't quite have the same ring to it), but this is alarming, must-see TV." —*One Motion Magazine*

"Forget about visiting your local movie theater for your horror fix this month. You'll find everything you need in Spark TV's *The Apple Hill Murders*: haunted houses, creepy killers, psycho girlfriends, and a powerhouse climax that pushes the boundaries of what can be shown on basic cable. Butter some popcorn and feel the blood splatter." — *Gore TV*

A note from BRANT KULCHNER, EXECUTIVE PRODUCER

The Apple Hill Murders premiered on December 15th, 2016, pulling in 18.2 million total viewers, breaking a basic cable ratings record, and cementing Spark TV as the leader in true-crime programming. A horrific descent into murder and madness, the docudrama earned stellar reviews from nearly every media outlet. It won awards (1 Emmy, 2 Golden Globes, and 1 Critics' Choice, to be exact), spawned several popular books and podcasts, and has become a bestseller on DVD, Blu-ray, and streaming platforms. Even the Northern California cabin where the killings took place has become a morbid travel destination for "dark tourists." As the definitive account of a story that shocked the country, *The Apple Hill Murders* was a historic television event and has since transformed into a cultural phenomenon.

Now, for the first time in print, Kulchner Productions and Underworld Press present *The Apple Hill Murders Companion*, a collection of archived materials previously available only in electronic format. Presented in narrative order, the documents include news articles, interviews, research papers, blogs, message boards, and the original script for *The Apple Hill Murders* telecast. But more than a guide to an unfathomable event, the book you now hold in your hands also shares a personal story. It chronicles the experiences of Cherie Alvarez,

Coral Harrington, and Paula Green—three best friends forced to confront a terrifying evil and whose sacrifices are impossible to forget.

Filled with secret histories and chilling revelations, *The Apple Hill Murders Companion* offers a fitting collective tribute to the young victims of this tragedy. The story you are about to experience will not always be an easy read, but it remains an even greater struggle for the survivors left behind in its wake.

—Brant Kulchner
Los Angeles, 2017

THE APPLE HILL MURDERS COMPANION

From "Pregnant Wife Slaughtered by Masked Home Intruder" (originally aired on KICU-TV's *Inside American Crime*, November, 2003, 17:00 ET):

THIS IS A RUSH TRANSCRIPT. THIS COPY MAY NOT BE IN ITS FINAL FORM AND MAY BE UPDATED.

WALTER BEAM, HOST: Folks, welcome to *Inside American Crime*, your one-stop shop for the latest in national crime headlines. No mindless chatter tonight. No fluff. We've got breaking news *now* and we're taking you to it. We're going live to Gilroy, an agricultural town a few hours outside San Francisco. Gilroy—my producer Lonnie says it's the "garlic capital of the world." It sure sounds like a nice place. But earlier today, in those quiet suburbs, police found the body of a woman, 29-year-old Gloria Alvarez, a wife and mother, beaten and battered to death with a claw hammer. And what's worse—Gloria was 16-weeks pregnant. She died protecting both the child in her womb and her 7-year-old daughter, who was home with her mother when a tall man wearing a skeleton mask burst through the front door and started ransacking the house. From there an explosive moment of violence ripped like a tornado through the home, leaving Gloria and her unborn child dead, and her little daughter, alive and holding back tears, hiding in a bedroom closet. With the murder suspect still on the loose, we go now to video footage of a community in shock.

(BEGIN VIDEO CLIP)

SOPHIE WHITEHEAD, NEIGHBOR: Nothing like this has ever happened here before. Police said it was a robbery gone wrong. I knew Gloria, her husband Mike…they have a daughter, a sweet little girl named Cherie. I can't talk right now! I can't believe it!

GRANT CLIFTON, NEIGHBOR: They're a nice family. Good, church-going people. Gloria was pregnant. She used to take walks in the park here with her daughter. They'd ride the swings and climb the rope bridge. Sometimes I'd see them watering flowers in the community garden. Gloria was a good mother.

(END VIDEO CLIP)

BEAM: Good evening, folks. I'm Walter Beam, and I want to thank you for tuning in tonight. Prepare for a bombshell of a story.

In the California suburbs, in a small farming community, a housepainter's 29-year-old wife, pregnant and home alone with their young daughter. A stranger enters the house, dressed in a filthy flannel shirt and dungarees, wearing a skull mask. Imagine it. Imagine the terror. And then, like a raging animal, he beats and kills the mother with a hammer, but the daughter survives. Police find her cowering in a back closet. Now, with the suspect on the run, anything is possible, and the poor town of Gilroy is in turmoil.

Let's go straight to the source—Officer Brandon Bitler of the Gilroy Police Department, who was one of the first respondents on the scene. Officer Bitler, what happened out there today?

BRANDON BITLER, POLICE OFFICER: We've had a few incidents in the more residential parts of town lately. Break-ins, robberies. Vandalism and car theft. What happened today, we believe, is an extension of those smaller crimes. Criminals get cocky. They take bigger risks. And this morning, one of them got stupid and took the life of a mother and her unborn child. We can only be thankful that the young daughter wasn't hurt. But we're here now, we're canvassing the neighborhood and searching the house for clues to the suspect's identity. We've got roadblocks on both sides of the highway, and we're making progress.

BEAM: Thank you, Officer Bitler. I want to put some pictures up as we go to Marcy Carrothers, senior news reporter for the *Santa Clara County Register*. Marcy, you've written about this case for the paper's afternoon edition. Take us back to the beginning. A young, pregnant wife beaten to death with a hammer by a man in a Halloween mask.

And police believe she died while trying to keep her 7-year-old daughter free from harm.

On your screen you're looking at pictures of the victim, Gloria Alvarez, just 29-years-old. A beautiful woman, curly brown hair down to her shoulders, glowing skin. The embodiment of an expectant mother. Her husband Mike, who police say was painting a house in another part of town when the murder took place, wants justice. We all want justice. Marcy, help us set the scene.

MARCY CARROTHERS, NEWS REPORTER: Walter, here's what we have learned so far from police. Gloria Alvarez was eating breakfast at home with her daughter. They had a fun day planned—a short hike, a picnic in the park, and a trip to see the butterflies at Gilroy Gardens. And then a man walked through the front door. He was wearing a mask—a cheap, rubber mask made to look like a rotting human skull. He took a hammer from his pocket and waved it at the mother and child, threatening to kill them if they moved an inch. He began tearing apart the living room, looking for money and jewelry. From there, detectives are still piecing together the tragic chain of events that followed.

BEAM: Marcy, we're looking at some exterior shots of the Alvarez residence now. A modest home, with a narrow driveway, a front lawn, some flowerbeds and a few overhanging trees. The house appears to be at the tail end of a cul-de-sac. Now, I don't see any vehicles in the driveway, which makes sense because the police are telling us that the husband takes the family truck when he goes to work. Now here's the amazing part—the child, the little girl. Only 7-years-old. We don't know whether she was forced into the closet by the killer, or if she ran and hid there on her own. But when she thinks it's safe to come out, she leaves the closet in search of her mother. And what she finds is nothing short of horrific—her mother's body crumpled in a corner, her body broken and ragged and covered in blood. And what does this brave little girl do? She does what her parents always told her to do if she suspected trouble. She calls 911 and asks for help. What an incredible story of courage and survival.

Officer Bitler, a question for you—just how off-the-charts savage was this murder? And were there signs of a struggle in the home?

BITLER: I'm hesitant to reveal too many details from the crime scene, but the killer used the claw end of the hammer to deliver some of the blows against Mrs. Alvarez. The hammer tore into her left eye socket, causing what is commonly known as a "blowout fracture," and she sustained fatal injuries to her head and neck. Fortunately, her daughter was not physically injured. We're still processing the house for evidence, including fingerprints, and hair and clothing fibers. We're studying surveillance footage taken from nearby gas stations and other businesses. We're going to catch this guy, Walter.

BEAM: I want to turn our attention to Jason Thompson, who lives with his family down the street from the victim's house. Jason serves as one of the block captains in the suburb where the murder took place. Along with a team of local citizens, it's his job to keep an eye on his community and contact law enforcement about anything suspicious in the neighborhood.

Jason, thank you for being with us tonight. Officer Bitler has told us that there has been a string of crimes in the area. What have you observed and can you draw any conclusions about the murder that took place this morning?

JASON THOMPSON, NEIGHBOR: First, let me say that we are in total shock tonight. Gloria was a kindhearted woman. She was so excited about being pregnant again. Her husband Mike is an honest man, a hard worker, and the best painter in town. His alibi checks out and has been corroborated by multiple witnesses. And their daughter is precious. An angel. They didn't deserve this.

It's true—there have been some burglaries in the neighborhood recently, but we've had no sightings of a man in a mask. We've had no acts of terror or violence.

BEAM: Now, Officer Bitler mentioned that detectives intend to study the surveillance footage of nearby businesses to see if their suspect shows up on any of the tapes. As block captain, do you know whether or not the Alvarez family had a home security system, possibly one with video?

THOMPSON: They had a home alarm installed, but I don't think they kept it on when one of them was inside the residence. Most of the houses in our neighborhood have security systems, and some have motion-activated cameras on the front porch. Police have been collecting that footage with the hope that the suspect got nabbed by one of our cameras.

BEAM: You know, I hate to bring this up because it's a very frightening possibility, but if what you're saying is true—if Mr. and Mrs. Alvarez kept their alarm system off while they were at home, then perhaps the intruder knew this. He knew their schedule—their routine. He picked a house at the end of the street—a house surrounded by shadowy trees. Maybe he had been stalking the property, waiting for the right moment to strike. And if the husband always took the truck to work, then the killer might have known when he was gone and when Gloria would be home alone with their daughter.

THOMPSON: That's a possibility, though I'm not sure why he would want to target Gloria. Or why he would be so brazen as to enter the house in broad daylight. There was no sexual assault, as far as I'm aware, and there's nothing to suggest that the suspect was in search of some expensive item that only the Alvarez family had. I'm sorry to say this, but I think a lot of the information in this case is going to come from the young daughter. Did the killer speak to her? If so, what did he say? Did the man ever take off his mask? These are all questions that only a terrified little girl can answer.

BEAM: Officer Bitler, I understand that you need to maintain the integrity of the investigation and withhold certain pieces of information from the general public. I hope you don't mind me asking—but where is the young daughter at this time? Has she provided any clues to the detectives working the case?

BITLER: The Alvarez daughter and her father have been at the Gilroy police station all day, speaking with detectives and providing much of the information you've just heard. The child has provided a description of the assailant to our sketch-artist, and we're sending that picture out to every media outlet in the area. Right now, I can tell you that the evidence suggests she did *not* witness the murder of her mother. We believe she was already safely inside the bedroom closet when the killing took place. For a girl of her age, considering the circumstances, she's extremely brave.

BEAM: Well, that's good news. I would hate to think of the long-term psychological effects that witnessing a parent's murder would have on a child. And, folks, we have that sketch up on your screen right now—a tall man wearing a dirty flannel, jeans, and a skeleton mask. The mask has clenched teeth and jagged eye-holes, the rubber around them cracked and stained. A terrifying image for anyone, let alone a pregnant mother and her 7-year-old daughter. The suspect is still on the loose and a manhunt in the San Francisco Bay Area remains in full force.

As we pause for a commercial break, let's take a moment to remember the lives that were tragically lost today. A wife and mother, 29-year-old Gloria Alvarez, and the unborn child that she had been carrying for 16 weeks. Tonight, her husband and daughter are asking for your prayers and your assistance. If you know anything about this awful crime, please contact the Gilroy Police Department in Northern California. A family in pain needs your help.

Thank you to my guests tonight, and to you—the audience—for watching and for caring. We'll be right back.

SALINAS—A 36-year-old homeless man police say beat a pregnant woman to death in Gilroy earlier this week has been arrested.

Alfred Mitchell was taken into custody Sunday morning at a homeless encampment on the banks of the Salinas River, authorities reported.

That same day, Santa Clara County prosecutors charged Mitchell with premeditated murder, first-degree murder of an unborn child, and assault with a deadly weapon, according to court records.

Two undercover officers with the Gilroy and Salinas police departments entered the homeless camp in the dawn hours Sunday and found Mitchell sleeping inside a makeshift tent, according to a court affidavit filed by Gilroy Police Officer Brandon Bitler.

Police found the hammer that they believe was used in the murder inside a cigar box that belonged to Mitchell, the report indicated. Buried nearby were the green flannel shirt and skeleton mask believed to have been worn by Mitchell during the attack. The shirt and mask were smeared with blood.

Online jail records reveal that Mitchell, who has a history of mental illness, was being held at the Monterey County Jail in Salinas on $850,000 bail.

The murder occurred around 9:00 a.m. last Wednesday morning in a quiet residential area of Gilroy. Surveillance footage taken from home security cameras shows the mask-wearing killer stalking the neighborhood before entering the home of the Alvarez family on Apache Court.

Authorities said Mitchell used a hammer to beat and kill Gloria Alvarez, 29, who was pregnant at the time of her death.

At some point before the attack, the Alvarez's 7-year-old daughter hid inside a bedroom closet and remained unharmed. After the suspect fled the scene, the daughter discovered her mother's body and called 911.

Police collected an extensive amount of evidence from the home, including blood samples and footwear impressions that the killer left behind.

Mitchell was identified as a result of the surveillance footage and a police-artist sketch based on a description provided by the Alvarez daughter.

"Insane or Just Evil: Finding the Truth in a Pack of Lies" by George Bruck (originally published in *Frontpage Crime Blog*, January, 2004):

Two months ago in Northern California, a man wearing a skeleton mask walked into a house in the town of Gilroy and struck down a pregnant woman with a hammer, taking her life and the life of her unborn child. Days later, police found suspect Alfred Mitchell, 36, in a hobo camp in Salinas and arrested him. When asked why he committed the murder, Mitchell told police that a female demon known as Lamashtu insisted that he carry out the crime.

Now that Mitchell's legal proceedings are underway, we have to ask ourselves: is the man mentally ill, or merely "prepping" for a trial in which he hopes acting crazy will set him free? According to press cuttings from tabloid rags like *The National Dish*, Mitchell has been causing disturbances in jail, screaming at all hours of the night and biting open his skin to give "blood offerings" to Lamashtu. His manic behavior begs a second question: can a murderer escape justice by pretending to be insane?

The insanity defense has been in existence since Greek and Roman times, so the idea that criminals might fake symptoms in order to avoid being executed is nothing new. As the field of psychology grew throughout the 19th century, criminals became more knowledgeable about insane behaviors and mannerisms, mimicking what they read in books or newspapers in an attempt to deceive authorities. Termed "malingerers," these criminals-cum-actors rarely succeeded in their ploys, and seasoned investigators, through the power of observation, were usually able to sniff out a faker within a few days. One telltale sign of a malingerer is that he is constantly breaking character to see if his behavior is having an effect on his captors, and it is through this transparency that his ruse eventually crumbles.

Though felony defendants rarely employ an insanity defense, there remains a fraction of wiggle room to pull it off and thereby avoid the death sentence. As Alfred Mitchell sits in his cell, talking to ghosts and picking at his scabs like the drooling Renfield from *Dracula*, one has to imagine that the temptation to appear mentally ill must be a powerful one. It is up to the forensic psychologist to study potential malingerers, analyze their symptoms, and compare them to the well-documented pathologies of those who have been deemed legally insane. Other factors—including the criminal's medical history, the examination of the crime scene, and the criminal's behavior after the crime was committed—are also critical in making this diagnosis.

In the violent beating of a pregnant mother, Mitchell wore a mask so that his face could not be identified. He wore gloves so to not leave his fingerprints at the scene. He fled from police and hid in a homeless camp to avoid capture. He buried two pieces of evidence that linked him to the crime. Are these the behaviors of a man trapped in the throes of a psychotic episode, or those of a cunning and sadistic killer?

Jailhouse interviews can also reveal a criminal's deception. A trained investigator may only need a few hours to pull back the façade and expose the malingerer behind it. Jonathan Lowe, professor of psychology at Monterey Peninsula College, says that law enforcement will often ask a suspect for detailed background information about his life before ever broaching the subject of a crime. This way, the suspect will be unable to manufacture past insane behaviors in order to justify his offense.

"Most criminals are terrible liars," says Lowe, who has been following the Mitchell case. "They learn how to act crazy from movies like *One Flew Over the Cuckoo's Nest* and *The Silence of the Lambs*."

One of the most common symptoms that malingerers attempt to replicate is the auditory hallucination, a common trope in psychological horror movies and dramatized TV shows. Alfred Mitchell claims that a demon ordered him to kill, but auditory hallucinations rarely originate from some sort of imaginary monster, and only a small percentage instruct a patient to lash out in specific ways. Lowe adds that malingerers often contradict their own beliefs, latch onto random delusions suggested by a police detective or forensic psychologist, or provide convenient alibis for their crimes that involve psychotic or hallucinatory experiences.

"Even if a person somehow manages to fake out a doctor or a police officer during an interrogation," says Lowe, "there are standardized tests that make this kind of deception almost impossible to sustain." Lowe explains that the tests, some of which can last for hours, are designed to catch malingerers in their own trap. "I don't want to say much more or else reveal all our secrets," he says. "A potential malingerer could end up reading your blog."

Lowe was unable to comment specifically on the Alfred Mitchell case, having not interviewed the suspect or read his case file or psychiatric report. However, Lowe questions some of Mitchell's more outrageous behavior, aligning it more with a psycho-killer from a Hollywood slasher film than with genuine mental illness.

"Blaming a murder on an imaginary demon is like claiming to suddenly have amnesia or multiple personalities," argues Lowe. "It's reflective of the myth-making behind mental illness, and I'd be surprised if a court in this country would fall for it."

COMMENTS:

Shay-Shay
15 min ago

We need to know more about Mitchell before we rush to judgment. What were his parents like? Did he suffer any abuse at home? Did he ever go to school? How did he interact with other kids? And how did Mitchell end up homeless? He's either truly insane and needs medical treatment, or he's just so evil that we can't even begin to label his actions.

Peter
9 min ago

I think he's a sick bastard who needs to be put down like a rabid dog. Our children aren't safe with maniacs like him running around.

Morris P
8 min ago

I agree with Peter. Mitchell ran from the cops! He tried to cover up his crimes! If he was mentally ill he would have no concept of right and wrong. He'd probably still be inside that house, drinking the dead woman's blood and wearing her panties. The courts better not fall for his shtick.

Anonymous
6 min ago

I've read a lot of books about serial killers and murderers. Charles Manson, Ted Bundy, Richard Ramirez. I just finished a book about Jeffrey Dahmer, the biggest nut-bag of them all. Here's a guy who boiled the heads of his victims. He took men back to his house and drugged and mutilated them. He put one of his victims in the bathroom and cut his head off. If anyone should have been locked up in the loony bin, it was this dude. My point is, you can't even begin to compare Dahmer and Alfred Mitchell. Mitchell was a homeless bum. He was probably looking for money to buy booze or drugs. Lock the creep up in prison and throw away the key.

Insane Brain
3 min ago

Degenerates like Dahmer and Mitchell are not an anomaly. We're surrounded by these kinds of people every day. And there's really no difference between them. One guy likes to butcher homosexuals. Another claims he's possessed by a demon that drove him to beat a pregnant woman to death with a hammer. But how do we draw the line between what we consider "illegal" and "criminal," and what we consider "evil" and "insane"?

Anonymous
Just now

In all this talk about whether or not Alfred Mitchell is insane, we're forgetting about something. There's a little girl out there who just lost her mommy. A little girl who's going to remember that awful morning for the rest of her life. My thoughts and prayers are with her today, not with the man who killed her mother.

"Salinas Man Declared Legally Insane in '03 Murder Case" by Georgia
Campbell (originally published in *The Gilroy Press*, October, 2005, p. 2-
3):

In a surprising court decision that has some members of a Gilroy
community reeling in shock, a Salinas man has been ruled not guilty by
reason of insanity in the beating death of a pregnant woman in 2003.

Prior to the killing, Alfred Mitchell, 38, had at one time been a
patient in a mental institution in Salinas. He will now spend the rest of
his life in a mental hospital unless at some point he is found to be sane
and competent to stand trial, said Santa Clara County District Attorney
Faith Nichols. Nichols chose not to reveal the exact nature of
Mitchell's diagnosis, but indicated that he has been "severely mentally
ill for many years and needs urgent and long-term medical care."

As part of his not-guilty-by-reason-of-insanity plea, Mitchell
admitted to committing the murder, which occurred in a residential
area of Gilroy. According to Nichols, Mitchell will be committed to a
hospital for the criminally insane.

"Before the judge could make the decision, the defendant had to
acknowledge that he had committed a crime," Nichols said.

After putting on a Halloween mask and wandering a suburban
neighborhood in the morning hours, Mitchell entered the home of
Mike and Gloria Alvarez. Mrs. Alvarez, 29-years-old and 16-weeks
pregnant, was home alone with their 7-year-old daughter.

Mitchell placed the child into a closet in the back of the house
before returning to the kitchen, where he struck Mrs. Alvarez with the
claw-end of a hammer and killed her and her unborn baby. He fled the
scene and was arrested by police days later, Nichols explained.

At the time of his arrest, Mitchell told investigators that his mind
had been taken over by Lamashtu, a mythological demon that
terrorized pregnant women and drank the blood of their children.
According to police documents, Mitchell said that Lamashtu lives in
an ancient volcanic field in Salinas and makes him commit terrible
deeds.

Mitchell was charged with felony murder and carrying a concealed weapon, but criminal proceedings against him were halted when the district attorney's office began to question his competency to stand trial.

As a result, Mitchell was committed to Monterey State Hospital, where mental health officials conducted periodic reviews of his mental status. In January of this year, after a lengthy examination of Mitchell's medical history and details from the murder case, it was determined that he was legally insane at the time that he killed Alvarez, Nichols said.

"He has psychotic episodes, visual and auditory hallucinations, and other symptoms of psychosis," Mitchell's attorney, Darrell White, said. "He understands what he did. He knows he wielded the hammer that killed the victim. But he believes a demon inhabited his body and made him do it. In this sense, Mr. Mitchell did not know that what he did was legally wrong, because he did not believe that he was in control of his actions."

The ruling has surprised and angered many Gilroy residents familiar with the case. Jason Thompson, 44, who was in charge of the neighborhood watch program in the community where the murder took place, has expressed outrage over the decision.

"Mitchell is pulling the wool over everyone's eyes," Thompson said. "He murdered Gloria in cold blood. It was vicious and disgusting. He wore a mask to hide his identity, not because he was possessed by a demon. This should have been a death penalty case!"

But people closest to the murder victim demonstrated an incredible amount of compassion when making their statements to the court. The victim's husband, Mike Alvarez, 40, agreed with the plea deal that will allow Alfred Mitchell to reside in a mental institution rather than spend the rest of his life in a prison cell.

"A lot of people don't understand this, but I have made the choice to forgive," Mr. Alvarez spoke before the court on the day before the ruling was passed down. "I can't live the rest of my life with hatred in my heart, and I want to honor my wife's life and the life of our second child. Helping this man get the medical attention he needs is one way to do that."

Mr. Alvarez also read a letter composed by his daughter, now 9. Written in pencil on lined yellow paper, the letter brought many in the courtroom to tears.

"Everyone has a good side and a good heart," the young girl's letter read. "Forgiving people that hurt us is hard, but it helps us love each other more."

The judge was equally moved by the gesture of forgiveness and mercy shown by Mr. Alvarez and his daughter.

"I've been a judge for over 15 years, and I've seen my share of human suffering pass through this courtroom," Santa Clara County Circuit Judge Michelle Huong said. "The defendant in this case did an atrocious thing, but today we judge him with dignity and with hope, rather than with malice. And perhaps that is the true meaning of justice."

Alfred Mitchell will return to court in April at which time a mental facility for his rehabilitation will be announced.

From *Christened in Blood: Cherie Alvarez and the Apple Hill Slayings* by Ricky Sheldon (originally published by True Crime House, May, 2016 p. 4-5):

As a child, Cherie Alvarez endured a tragedy almost beyond human comprehension—a grisly, Technicolor nightmare of violence and death. From her hiding spot in a dark bedroom closet, Cherie must have heard her mother beg for her life. She must have heard her mother cry and scream. She must have heard the beating. She must have heard the hammer smash through flesh and bone, spraying her mother's blood onto the walls and floor...

In the countless newspaper and magazine articles about her case, reporters have not been able to resist drawing parallels between the murder of Cherie's mother and the slayings in Apple Hill over a decade later. But viewing Cherie through the troubled lens of her past has only served to muddle her perception in the media. As a victim of tragedy and subsequent bullying at school, how aware was Cherie of the severe psychological conflicts brewing inside her? Exactly what was her intent at Apple Hill? Was she pushed too far, the killings her only means of survival? Or was she death-obsessed from the start, her actions a manifestation of past trauma, morbid compulsions, and long-simmering rage?

In the straight-to-DVD horror film, *The Violation of Cherry Gonzalez*, writer and director Sam "Spooky" Etchinson responds to this latter question by refashioning the Cherie Alvarez story into a fictionalized and gore-soaked melodrama. The end result is a vulgar attempt at exploitation cinema, with cheap special effects, tasteless sexualized violence, and some of the worst acting ever committed to celluloid. Throughout the low-budget film, Etchinson depicts "Cherry Gonzalez" as the paradigm of an obsessive and deranged personality—a bullied loner with a nasty grudge against the world. While some critics of Cherie Alvarez subscribe to this fabrication of her character, *The Violation of Cherry Gonzalez* is specifically designed to mislead the public into believing that Cherie is a sociopath. And, unsurprisingly,

Etchinson is not alone in his penchant for tabloid mythmaking. Other interpretations of this dark tale—including Jonathan Rake's non-fiction novel *Blood Offerings*—have deliberately played fast and loose with the facts of Cherie's life, blurring the line between truth and fiction and turning tragedy into slick, glossy, and over-produced entertainment...

On the opposite side of the spectrum, Brant Kulchner's televised docudrama, *The Apple Hill Murders*, set to premiere in October of this year, promises to provide an unflinching portrayal of that fatal encounter in the Apple Hill woods. Unlike cheap horror flicks that turned Cherie's story into sleazy urban legend, the Kulcher production will hopefully give meaning to what low-brow hacks have considered just another third-rate slasher story...

"Demonic Shocker: A True California Horror Story!" by S.K. Robbins (originally published in *The National Dish* Online Edition, April, 2008):

Sunlit skies, garlic crops, and rolling cattle pastures. A farmland community and a one-story home nestled among apple trees and pink geraniums. It is from this bucolic setting in Northern California that Darcy Condale, 14, ran screaming one cold October night.

"It's the kill house, the ghost house, and everybody knows it," Darcy says today as she stands on the sidewalk near the infamous property on Apache Court in Gilroy. "What happened there was nasty. Even after all these years, evil can never be erased!"

As dusk falls on the quaint suburb, moonlit shadows hover like specters over the houses, creating ghostly shapes that make the hazel-eyed Darcy shiver. Fearful, she turns away from the darkened home at the end of the street. "Lamashtu hammered a woman to death in that house—splattered her blood and brains all over the wall. And I heard her baby got ripped right out of the womb! Now the demon haunts the place at night. And if you get too close, Lamashtu possesses your mind and makes you go crazy."

Even the most devoted ghost-hunters might have a hard time believing all the paranormal terrors that Darcy and other Gilroy teens say they've seen outside that home, including drops of blood floating in the air and skeletal handprints appearing on the doors. But no one can deny the reality of what happened in the fall of 2003, when a moment of horrendous violence turned this humble abode into a blood-drenched house of horrors.

On a chilly November morning, a pregnant mother was ravaged to death with a hammer, the weapon ripping through her scalp and skull and killing her and her unborn child. As the murderer—dressed in a dirty clothes and a skeleton mask—committed his senseless act of rage, the mother's 7-year-old daughter crouched in a nearby closet, her fear so intense that she wet herself in mute terror while the psychopath fled the house and escaped.

The murder stunned and horrified the Gilroy neighborhood. Residents began locking their doors and windows at night, purchasing expensive security systems, and growing suspicious of any stranger who happened to be passing through their quiet agricultural town. Ghosts or not, the killing continued to haunt the area—eventually turning the vicious homicide into a twisted urban legend. Like Hannibal "the Cannibal" Lecter from *The Silence of the Lambs*, the blood-craving lunatic was soon captured by police and sentenced to life in an insane asylum.

"It was an awful tragedy for the family and the community," says Matthew Larkin, director of the Gilroy Historical Museum and the author of *The Ghosts of Monterey County*. "Before police found out who did it, people were scared to go outside. Parents walked their kids to and from school and refused to let them play in the streets after dark. And then, even after the killer was caught, there was a change in the air. No one felt safe anymore.

"Gilroy has always prided itself on the camaraderie of its neighbors," adds Larkin. "But something broke down on that terrible morning, and no one knows how to fix it."

Yes, that terrible morning—when a homeless man named Alfred Mitchell donned a rubber skeleton mask and walked into the home of Mike and Gloria Alvarez, his sole intent to rob and to kill. With Mr. Alvarez away at work, Mitchell quickly took control of the scene. While holding the pregnant Mrs. Alvarez at bay with a hammer, Mitchell overturned tables, shattered a glass flowerpot and vase, and ransacked drawers and cupboards. Frothing at the mouth and claiming to be possessed by a female demon called Lamashtu, the assailant stuffed jewelry into his pockets and demanded that Mrs. Alvarez give him any cash that the family kept in their home. When Mrs. Alvarez offered her pocketbook with only a few dollar bills inside, it was then that police say the ghastly horror truly began.

The crime scene report reveals that the killer ordered Mrs. Alvarez, only 29-years-old at the time, onto her knees. Mitchell then proceeded to batter the defenseless woman with the flat end of the hammer, crushing the bones in her face and rendering her nearly unconscious. He then cinched her hands behind her back with his belt and began wielding the hammer with the claw side facing downward.

What followed was a savage beating that some Gilroy police officers say resulted in the most gruesome crime scene they have ever encountered.

"It was a cold and merciless act upon a helpless woman, a pregnant wife and mother," says Officer Leonard Parks. "There was blood everywhere—on the wall, on the carpet, on a family picture hanging on the wall. Mitchell stepped in the blood—sort of danced around in it and smeared it wherever he could. We tracked his bloody footprints throughout the house."

Officer Parks rubs his bearded chin, shuddering as he recalls the murder scene. "The victim's shirt had ridden up above her waist, and I noticed that she was pregnant. Her womb had been ripped apart," he says. "And that's when I knew that the perpetrator was a cold-blooded, psychopathic killer."

The body was discovered by the Alvarez daughter, who was brave enough to sneak out of the closet in an effort to help her mother. With the charnel stench of sudden death lingering in the air, the child walked barefoot through the blood to find her mother's shattered face gazing up at her like some macabre tableaux.

Courageously, the terrified girl scrambled to the phone and dialed 911, telling the dispatcher, "My mommy's been hurt." Once in the custody of Gilroy police and her father, the child helped a sketch artist draw a composite of the masked killer, which ultimately led to the madman's arrest at a nearby homeless camp.

"I can't imagine what it was like to find her mother like that," says Officer Parks, his steely blue eyes clouding with anger.

The slain woman's husband, Mike Alvarez, 42, has told reporters that his daughter is "doing as well as can be expected," but sources close to the family have noticed "startling changes" in the child that suggest an underlying psychological disturbance may be brewing.

"The father puts up a good act, but there's a crack in that family that's only going to get bigger as time goes on," says a family friend. "You don't experience that kind of evil in the world and walk away unaffected. That kind of evil leaves a mark. It leaves scars."

Darcy Condale and her friends believe the evil still thrives, emanating like a supernatural force from the yellow-trimmed house on Apache Court.

After the brutal murder occurred, rumors began circulating that a vindictive spirit had possessed Alfred Mitchell and had driven him to kill. According to town scuttlebutt, that same spirit now haunts the Alvarez home, threatening to harm anyone who ventures near.

Dubbed "The Demon House" by local youth, the residence often appears unoccupied, tucked away at the end of the block, the lights turned off and the blinds closed. Once kids began daring each other to step onto the property late at night, homeowner Mike Alvarez grew increasingly private, doing his best to shield his daughter from the unwanted attention.

Darcy says that in addition to seeing floating blood-drops and skeletal handprints outside the house, she once heard the sound of a hammer cracking against bone and a woman's unearthly screams coming from somewhere on the property.

Other young locals, including 17-year-old Timothy Bromley, say they have heard phantom moans and cult-like chanting when walking past the Alvarez residence late at night. "The house is damned, a real portal into hell," Timothy says. "I don't understand why the family insists on living there."

Despite the ghost stories that continue to plague the area and the Alvarez family, other Gilroy residents are quick to reject even the faintest suggestion that the paranormal has descended upon their quiet community.

"It's an insult to Mike and his daughter, and to the memory of Gloria," says Shannon Montgomery, 44, who lives near the Alvarez family. "If you ask me, Alfred Mitchell should be rotting away the rest of his life in prison, not living in some plush mental facility."

And it is the memory of Gloria Alvarez that most concerns Sam "Spooky" Etchinson, 27, an independent filmmaker from Salinas who has plans to make a motion picture about the savage murder and the capture of the deranged Alfred Mitchell.

Even though Mike Alvarez and his daughter are still living at the house, Etchinson says, the mother's ghost exists in torment, her murder so abhorrent that her spirit has not been able to make the transition into heaven.

"She's trapped on this earthly plane. She's in great pain, like King Hamlet's ghost. That's why she's screaming," explains Etchinson. "My fear is that her misery will grow to the point where she feels compelled to lash out at the innocent people around her."

Even if the Alvarez family moves away from Apache Court, Etchinson says, the victim's ghost will continue to be restless, a mournful spirit wandering aimlessly throughout the gloomy house. "A priest could perform a spiritual cleansing of the house, which might give the ghost the encouragement to move on," Etchinson suggests. "But I have faith that my movie will lead to some kind of closure, both for the mother's spirit and the daughter she left behind."

COMMENTS:

DarcyCondale
15 min ago

Can you say local celebrity? I know, I know, I'm a bitch, right? Whatever!

Anonymous
13 min ago

Celebrity? Try media whore instead. You should be ashamed for exploiting a nice girl and her family. Do you ever stop to think that Cherie Alvarez has feelings? Do you ever stop to think—at all?

SpookyEtchinson
11 min ago

Thank you to The National Dish for the shout-out! Make sure to visit my official website to get all the latest news on my movie! It's going to be dope!

Suspiria
9 min ago

Evil spirits do exist. And one of them lives in that house.

Anonymous
7 min ago

If evil spirits are real, Suspiria, then surely their existence would have been verified by scientists long ago. Give it up. This is just lazy journalism, spurred on by a bunch of bratty, attention-starved kids who have nothing better to do than mock the tragedy of others. You should delete your inane post.

PachecoPass
5 min ago

Gloria Alvarez was my friend. To think that a loving woman's home is now being called a "blood-drenched house of horrors" is reprehensible. We can blame it on the tabloids with their stories of demons and haunted houses, and we can blame it on careless pre-teens who don't give a crap about anyone except themselves. But the real person at fault here is Alfred Mitchell. Let's not forget that this is a stone-cold killer who now resides in a state-funded hospital. And we, as taxpayers, are footing the bill for his treatment. That's some warped kind of justice right there!

Anonymous
4 min ago

"That kind of evil leaves a mark. It leaves scars." I go to school with Cherie and she's perfectly fine. If you shove this story in her face and act all ignorant and mean, she won't let you get away with it. But if you're a nice person then she's cool.

HomeroomQueen
3 min ago

Check yourself, Anonymous. Cherie Alvarez pulled a weapon on my best friend—one of those keychains with a hidden knife on it. She nearly slashed my girl's throat. Cherie "the Freak" Alvarez deserves every bit of ridicule she gets.

Anonymous
2 min ago

I saw that fight and you're dead wrong, HomeroomQueen. That's not how it went down and you know it. You're lucky Cherie doesn't kick your stupid ass.

HomeroomQueen
1 min ago

I'd like to see her try. She's the biggest loser in the entire school. Dressing all in black and wearing those stupid purple shoes. I wouldn't be surprised if that mental case winds up dead just like her mother.

Anonymous
Just now

You fucking bitch. You better hope I don't find out who you are.

The Alvarez home on Apache Court, now haunted by a terrible crime

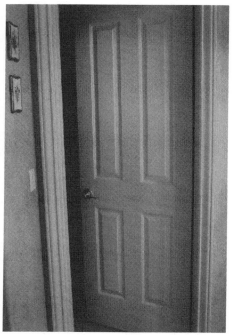

The bedroom closet where Cherie Alvarez hid from a psychotic killer

The homeless camp where confessed murderer Alfred Mitchell once lived

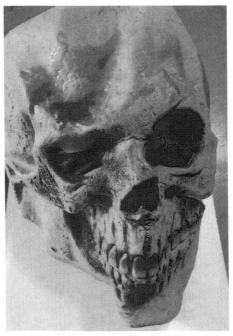

Halloween mask worn by Alfred Mitchell during the murder of Gloria Alvarez

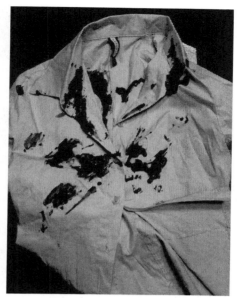

Evidence from the crime scene: Gloria Alvarez's blouse, soaked in blood

Evidence from the crime scene: the hammer used in the murder,
its handle streaked with blood

From *The Violation of Cherry Gonzalez* by Sam Etchinson (final shooting script, Fall, 2008):

EXT. – SUBURBAN NEIGHBORHOOD – AFTERNOON

HALLOWEEN in the dusty farming town of Gilroy, California. JACK-O'-LANTERNS and SCARECROWS line every front porch. BEDSHEET GHOSTS swing from every clothesline. OCTOBER LEAVES skitter across every road.

EXT. – GILROY MIDDLE SCHOOL – SAME AFTERNOON

The school bell rings and CHILDREN pour out into the courtyard, many of them dressed in costumes ranging from Dracula and the Werewolf to Iron Man and the Incredible Hulk.

As the children gather in cliques, PRINCIPAL CONRAD, 45, picks up a microphone from the sound booth and clears his throat.

                    PRINCIPAL CONRAD
    Quiet down, children, quiet down. And welcome
    to our 11th annual Halloween costume contest!
    Our judges are taking their seats and in just a
    few minutes we'll be asking kids who wish to
    participate to come forward.
    While you wait, have a listen to that timeless
    Halloween anthem from 1962, Bobby "Boris" Pickett
    and the original "Monster Mash"!

"Monster Mash" blares over the PA system and a few of the children start boogieing to the pop-culture hit.

EXT. - GILROY MIDDLE SCHOOL - RECESS FIELD - SAME AFTERNOON

Leaning against a chain-link fence is CHERRY GONZALEZ, 12, a lonely, pale drip of a girl. Wearing a black dress, with a black-ribbon bow around her neck and a white streak in her hair, she is the spitting image of LILY MUNSTER.

Assured that no one else is around, Cherry reaches into her backpack and takes out a RUSTY POCKETKNIFE. She tries out different grips on the blade, feeling its weight. She practices several stabbing motions through the air. Then she tests the blade against her palm, careful not to break the skin...

                    VOICE (O.S.)
          Hey, Murder Girl.

Cherry looks up to see BLAIR and ANITA, two blondes with candy-pink nail polish. Cherry hides the knife behind her back but it's too late--the other girls have spotted it.

                    ANITA
          What you got there, Murder Girl? Let us see it.

                    CHERRY
          No. It's private.

                    BLAIR
          Show it to us or we'll make you flash
          Charlie Cahill your underwear again.

                    ANITA
          Your choice, Murder Girl.

                    CHERRY
          No. And stop calling me that.

                    BLAIR
Who you supposed to be, anyway? Elvira?
Fuckin' Morticia Adams?

                    CHERRY
Lily Munster.

                    BLAIR
Who the fuck's Lily Munster?

                    CHERRY
She's the matriarch of the Munster family.
Don't you know anything?

                    BLAIR
(gets in Cherry's face)
Show us the knife right now or we'll beat
your skinny little ass. I'm not fucking
around.

Jaw clenched, Cherry brings the knife out from behind
her back. Blair grins at the sight of it, but Anita
looks uneasy...

                    BLAIR (CONT'D)
And just what the fuck do you think you're
gonna do with that?

                    CHERRY
I'll...I'll use it to defend myself. If you
try to hurt me again...I'll stab you with it.

Blair glances at Anita with a smirk.

                    BLAIR
Oh, really? Well, let me tell you what I
think...I don't think you're gonna do a
damn thing with that knife. I don't think
you have the guts.

                    ANITA
          Blair, let's go. The costume contest is
          gonna start soon.

                    BLAIR
          Shut up, Anita. We're not going anywhere
          until Murder Girl gives me what I want.
                    (to Cherry)
          You heard me. Hand it over.

Cherry holds her ground. She clutches the knife in one
trembling hand, pointing it at Blair.

                    BLAIR (CONT'D)
          Last chance, Murder Girl.

Cherry swallows hard. She's struggling to be brave. She
digs her shoes into the soft grass.

                    BLAIR (CONT'D)
          Okay. Fine. I didn't want to be the one to
          tell you this, but you give me no choice.
                    (beat)
          You stink, Murder Girl. That's why no one
          likes you, why no one sits next to you in
          class and why you eat lunch by yourself.
          You smell. You fuckin' reek.

                    ANITA
          Hey, come on, Blair...

Cherry doesn't move. Her hand shakes. Her eyes are wide,
brimming with tears. Blair stares Cherry down.

                    BLAIR
          You stink like trash. Like shit left in
          the bowl for too long...

Cherry is trembling. The knife glints in the sun.
There's one long, agonizing beat as Blair draws out the
moment...

BLAIR (CONT'D)
And most of all? You stink like your
mother's rotting corpse.

SLAM! With sudden, fluid grace CHERRY HAS SMASHED BLAIR
INTO THE FENCE, gripping her by the throat with one
hand and pressing the knife against her neck.

CHERRY
Feel that, you peroxide piece of trash?
Feels cold, doesn't it? Cold and sharp.

BLAIR
Let me go, you crazy bitch!

Cherry runs the blade gently along Blair's neck.

ANITA
I'm getting Principal Conrad!

Anita runs off. With tears in her eyes, Cherry prods
the blade against Blair's jugular vein. She doesn't
want to hurt her...but...

CHERRY
How do you feel now, cunt?

BLAIR
I'm...I'm scared.

Cherry presses the blade more firmly against Blair's
throat.

BLAIR (CONT'D)
Please don't hurt me.

                    CHERRY
        I'm not gonna hurt you. But if that
        herpes-spreading, cock-sucking mouth of
        yours ever mentions my mother again, I'll
        fucking kill you. You understand?

                    BLAIR
        Yes.

                    CHERRY
        Louder!

                    BLAIR
                    (sobbing)
        Yes!

                    CHERRY
        Good. Now let me see you smile.

Cherry SLASHES THE BLADE DOWN HARD AND DEEP across
Blair's cheek. Blair drops to the ground, BLOOD GUSHING
from the wound. She starts to SCREAM...blood fills her
mouth and seeps through her fingers...

Cherry is wide-eyed, shocked and fascinated by the
gore. Blair lies crumpled on the ground, CRYING--

Cherry stares at the knife in her hand. She runs her
finger along the blade, gathering blood on her
fingertip. She TASTES THE BLOOD AND SMILES. And then--

--A SECURITY GUARD GRABS CHERRY FROM BEHIND, dragging
her to the ground. Principal Conrad stands nearby,
terrified.

                    PRINCIPAL CONRAD
        Careful! She's got a knife!

                    CHERRY
        Let go of me, asshole!

                    SECURITY GUARD
          Hold still! Stop resisting!

Now, in SLOW MOTION, Cherry becomes a writhing animal-
-limbs flailing, teeth gnashing. Spittle flies from her
mouth...

The security guard wrenches the knife from Cherry's
hand... throws it into the grass...he PINS Cherry onto
her stomach, YANKS HER ARMS BEHIND HER BACK...but he's
too strong, too rough...he accidentally BREAKS HER
WRIST--

                    SECURITY GUARD
          Oh shit—

...and Cherry SCREAMS, mouth gaping, eyes rolled
upwards, drowning out all other sounds as we...

                                    CUT TO BLACK.

From "Bullying Incident Sparks Need for Change" by Henry Slater (originally published in *The Gilroy Press*, November, 2008, p. 2):

Gilroy Union Middle School District administrative officials have suspended two students after an incident of bullying that occurred at their upper middle school.

The superintendent for the district, David Pedrini, stated that two students were suspended due to acts of verbal cruelty and physical violence against another student.

"We take incidents like this very seriously," Pedrini said, adding that the bullying took place during the school's annual Halloween costume contest. "There's no place for violence or intimidation in our classrooms and schoolyards. As a school district and as a community, we refuse to stand for it."

The victim's father, who will remain anonymous in this article in order to protect his 12-year-old daughter's identity, has come forward with startling details about the incident. The father said his daughter was enjoying the costume contest with her friends when two other students began taunting her and calling her names.

"All of the kids were in costume, getting ready for the contest and listening to music, having a good time," the father said. "And then this happened."

The father said his daughter was taunted, punched, and shoved into a row of lockers. He said that one of the attackers, a female student, mimicked holding a hammer and made a "smashing" gesture inches from his daughter's face.

"There's a back-story to this event that is very painful for my daughter," the father explained. "This was more than a physical assault. This was an assault on my daughter's emotions and on her heart."

The father indicated that he was pleased with the school district's swift and just response to the incident. "They really care about our kids," the father said.

Pedrini would not answer specific questions about the incident, including the level of violence that occurred or the reasons why the victim was singled out. "However, I'm aware of the motivations in this attack, and frankly, I'm disgusted and angered by them," he said.

The bullying incident is being investigated by police, said Office Brandon Bitler of the Gilroy Police Department. "We're looking into whether a physical injury was sustained by the victim. There may have been a knife involved, so we're checking out that angle as well," Officer Bitler stated. "This is one of many instances of bullying that have taken place with students in the district lately, so we're deeply concerned.

"We stand by the people in our community, especially our children," Officer Bitler also said.

In an attempt to provide a safe learning environment for all students, Pedrini said the district will be holding an emergency meeting to review and possibly revise its bullying and harassment policies. "We are always looking for ways to improve the safety conditions of our schools, including the ways students interact with each other," he said. "We're going to have a student-panel at the meeting so that we can hear their concerns and ideas."

Coral Harrington, a seventh-grader in the district and close friend of the victim in this incident, said that the upper-grade students are already one step ahead of the school district. As part of a class project, they have created a writing contest that will give students the opportunity to write stories and poems about real or fictional experiences with bullying.

"The English department is looking into the school budget to see what kind of awards we can give for the contest, and how we can continue to promote awareness of this important issue," Harrington said. "We want to hold rallies and community events that let people know how they can stop bullying when they see it.

"My friend is the strongest person I know," Harrington added. "She's nice and funny. She's kind to other people. She turns the other cheek, even after all she's been through."

From the clinical examination of Cherie Alvarez (reprinted here with permission from the Alvarez family and Chamberlains Mental Health Services, Gilroy, 2009):

Edith H. Montgomery, Ph.D.
Clinical Psychology
Chamberlains Mental Health Services
8000 Church Street # C
Gilroy, California 95020

Name: Cherie Alvarez, age 13
Date of Birth: 09/1/1995
Date of Testing: 09/14/2009

PSYCHOLOGICAL TESTING RESULTS

Referral History: Cherie is currently in the eighth grade at the Gilroy Middle School in Gilroy, California. She was referred by Dr. Stanley Trotter, the school psychologist, for a psychological evaluation in order to determine her cognitive skills and to ascertain the causes for some of her problems in school. These problems include irrational or impulsive behavior that has led to arguments with classmates and at least two physical altercations on campus. One of Cherie's physical fights at school allegedly involved a self-defense keychain with an internal knife blade that she pressed against a classmate's cheek.

Scope of Evaluation: Over the course of two sessions, Cherie was given the WISC-IV to obtain her intellectual profile. Cherie was also administered the Koppitz-2 to assess visual-motor functioning and to diagnosis any developmental disorders. She was given a battery of projective tests to determine her current emotional health.

Impression and Test Behavior: Cherie is a pretty, friendly and outgoing girl, tall and lean for her age, with light, auburn-colored hair to her shoulders and a vibrant smile. Her manner was upbeat and she laughed easily and demonstrated mature conversational skill during the opening interview. Cherie expressed little reservation about being subjected to various test situations, viewing the procedures more as a day off from school than a serious examination of her troubles and her propensity for fighting. She was enthusiastic about her extracurricular activities and spoke kindly about a good friend named "Coral," but she was reticent to discuss the topic of violence and changed the subject when the death of her mother was brought up. "A book on the kitchen table—one of those lift-the-flap books about dogs. That's all I remember—that and the closet. It was dark, my eyes were closed, and I was hiding," Cherie said when asked what she saw on the morning of her mother's murder. In spite of these obstacles, she was cooperative and cordial, expressing an interest in the psychology at work behind the testing.

Regarding school incidents having to do with fighting or bullying, Cherie complained that she feels "like an outcast" and that she has often felt "scared and alone" on campus. She adamantly denied ever bringing a knife to school and rejected any suggestion of her being a violent or aggressive person. In between testing, during one of her quieter moments, Cherie said, "I miss my mom," and she began to cry softly. After taking a short break, Cherie talked freely about her interest in the arts, including books and movies, and she showed advanced expressive language skills for a girl of her age. She spoke glowingly of her father and commented many times on the strength of their relationship.

Intellectual Functioning: Cherie's intellectual ability lies in all verbal areas. She reasoned well, spoke clearly, and demonstrated a strong grasp of both basic and advanced logical concepts. She possesses good visual analysis skills and would achieve strong results in artistic design and creative writing. Near the end of the non-verbal section of testing, however, Cherie did grow restless and her behavior bordered on unpredictable. She paced the room, cracked her knuckles, and at one point stood in the corner and refused to speak.

Emotional Functioning: Cherie's difficulties in responding to some of the more structured parts of the test parallel the unpredictability and impulsiveness of her behavior. Although she is a highly intelligent girl and cares a great deal about the important people in her life, her past trauma has limited her social skills and her awareness of the boundaries that exist among human beings. The fluctuation of her impulse control has made certain aspects of the school setting difficult, especially in terms of conflict resolution with those she would consider her enemies. "Cats and dogs have always been natural enemies," Cherie said during the closing interview. "It makes sense that people would have enemies, too."

An analysis of Cherie's responses to projective testing reveals an inhibition to her thoughts and fantasies about the world. She does not always readily see and accept boundaries and she often views certain situations from an extreme point of view. At times she had trouble concentrating and seemed to blot out memories that troubled her. Cherie also has the tendency to classify people, places, and experiences into very general categories, a limitation that could lead to psychological problems later in her life. The results of her projective tests reveal additional psychological values that underscore Cherie's difficulty in resolving conflicts with others.

Although Cherie engages in some distorted thinking, she remains an inquisitive and creative young girl. If she continues to look at others through the tunnel vision of her own life experiences, she may develop social anxiety or paranoia as she gets older. However, through continued psychotherapy, Cherie is more than capable of developing into a mature and confident young adult and someone able to resolve conflicts without using violence.

Edith Montgomery

Edith H. Montgomery, Ph.D.
Clinical Psychologist

"The Canopy," a short story by Cherie Alvarez (written for a Teens Against Bullying Writing Competition, Spring, 2010):

The walk home was long and lonely, the falling October sun making ghostly shadows in the trees. Kevin Miller thought that even the birds perched on their branches looked sad, their wings crusted with dirt and their beaks empty of food. As Kevin walked alone, he could hear the cruel laughter of his classmates as they trotted behind him.

"What a cry baby," one of them said.

"Chicken shit," another muttered.

Fighting back tears, Kevin put his head down and focused on the weeds that sprouted up through the concrete. He hurried as fast as he could to his house on West Knoll Road.

Kevin always had a hard time making friends. He was short and potato-shaped. He wore clunky prescription glasses and second-hand clothes. He kept his sandy-brown hair long and flat, and big strands of it were always flopping into his face. Kevin never performed well in sports; he was always dropping the ball, missing the ball, or throwing the ball out of bounds. The other kids laughed at him. They had been laughing at him for a very long time.

I really am chicken shit, Kevin thought, turning into his driveway. He was now far away from the other kids, far away from those whose words often hurt more than their fists.

Standing outside his front door, Kevin took a moment to catch his breath. He turned his face to the gusty wind, allowing it to cool the sweat that had broken out in little drops on his forehead. He thought the wind would also help to dry the tears under his eyes. If his parents were home, he didn't want them to see that he had been crying (his dad especially—no crying was one of the house rules). Doing his best to forget the awful memory of that day, he swept his hair out of his face and went inside.

Buddy Bradley turned left at the liquor store, still clutching the rubber mask in his fist. At the corner he stopped outside the thrift shop to look at the costumes in the window. Halloween was Buddy's favorite time of year. He liked scaring all the little kids at school with tales of thirsty vampires, bug-eyed aliens, and crazy murderers. Chuckling to himself, Buddy continued down the road. It had been a great day—his teachers had left him alone, he stole a dollar from Mrs. Holloway's swear jar, and best of all, he humiliated that blubber-guts Kevin Miller, the biggest chicken in the entire 7th grade.

"Hey, Buddy, you laughin' at your own reflection?"

Buddy had been so caught up in his thoughts that he hadn't realized that one of his crew, Terence Jones, was beside him.

"Nah, man," said Buddy. "I was just thinking about what we pulled on Miller today. Instant classic."

"Seriously," Terence said, laughing. "I mean, it's Halloween, you think he wouldn't get so freaked out by some stupid monster mask."

"The guy's a pussy," Buddy said.

"And did you hear him scream when you snuck up behind him with that thing on? Just like a little girl," Terence said.

"Little faggot is more like it," Buddy said. He slapped palms with Terence and turned in the direction of the railroad tracks. He lived with his mother at the Whistle Stop trailer park just a few blocks away.

Kevin's parents had left him a note on top of a cardboard box of pizza in the refrigerator. Kevin gobbled down a slice of pepperoni and olive as he read the sloppy handwriting that told him they had gone to the bar down the street. As he reached for another greasy slice, Kevin felt a wave of relief wash over him. Now he had the entire house to himself and wouldn't have to put up with any stupid questions about how his day at school had gone.

As Kevin sat down at the kitchen table to finish his math homework, his mind began to wander. He liked math—he was really good at fractions and long division—but it was impossible for him to complete the worksheet. Instead, he grabbed another slice of pizza (the last one) and began replaying the afternoon over in his mind, the events unwinding like scenes from a movie he never wanted to see.

Kevin heard the laughter first—but he ignored his classmates and tried to pay attention to the interesting shapes that Mr. Evans, their art teacher, was drawing on the board. Then he felt a hand on his shoulder, the fingernails sharp as razor blades, yanking him backward in his seat. Kevin found himself staring into the most hideous face he had ever seen—a face of burned skin, melting eyeballs, and broken teeth. Kevin screamed. He turned around in his seat and lunged forward, trying to escape the monster that was surely going to kill him. And then he fell—right out of his chair and onto the floor—just as Buddy Bradley took off his monster mask and Mr. Evans yelled at everyone to be quiet. Buddy stashed the mask into his backpack before their teacher could really understand what had happened, but Kevin knew that the entire class had seen and heard his reaction. Even worse, they were in on the joke. Tears fell from Kevin's eyes as he stumbled out of the room. He spent the rest of the day in the nurse's office, pretending to have a stomachache.

Kevin crumpled his math worksheet in his fist, imagining that the paper was Buddy's head. He imagined all of Buddy's blood and pink, glistening chunks of his brain leaking through his fingers and clumping into a disgusting pile on the kitchen table. Then Kevin broke one of the other house rules—he started swearing. He shouted and he screamed, using every curse word he had ever heard in his life, all the words that his father told him never to use (but then used himself all the time). He cursed his parents for giving birth to him, and he cursed God for making him ugly and weak. Before he exhausted himself and collapsed in a heap on the kitchen floor, he cursed Buddy Bradley and made a silent vow to teach him a lesson he would never forget.

"Pass the ketchup," Buddy's mother said in her usual sad voice. Buddy sat across from her at the card table in the kitchenette. Buddy handed her the sticky bottle of Heinz 57.

"I don't think the meat's cooked all the way," Buddy said, using a fork to jostle the hamburger patty around on his plate. "There's all this red juice, Mom. It looks like blood."

Buddy's mother didn't say anything. Sighing, she smothered her hamburger patty in ketchup and picked at her food. Buddy dipped a slice of bread into the ketchup and ate that instead of his hamburger. Then he got up from the table and dumped his plate in the kitchen sink. As he went into his bedroom to listen to some music, Buddy realized just how much he missed their old house. It was one of many things that he missed, one of the many things that he could never get back, no matter how much he prayed to God he could never—

Stop it, Buddy scolded himself. *Only sissies think like that. Just put on some Metallica and be a man.*

Kevin stood in the back of the closet, next to his mother's cocktail dresses and his father's military jackets. He knew where the footlocker was—on the top shelf, its busted lid wrapped with thick rubber bands. He took the footlocker down, sat on the floor, unwound the rubber bands, and opened the lid. His father's pistol sat among a clutter of poker chips and strange coins. Kevin picked up the gun and held it in his hand. It always surprised him how light it felt. Holding the weapon, he walked into his father's office where they kept the family computer. Carefully, Kevin put the gun on the desk. Then he logged onto the Internet. After searching through a few websites, he found what he was looking for. He picked up the phone on the desk and dialed the number.

Buddy's mother was already asleep on the couch when the phone rang. Buddy hurried to the little table in the hallway, the one underneath the portrait of his father, and picked up the receiver.

"It's Terence," said the rough-sounding voice. "Meet me at the canopy at eight. Got something wicked to show you."

"Terence? That you?" Buddy asked.

"I said it was, didn't I? I gotta go. Don't be late."

Buddy hung up the phone. He didn't think the voice on the phone sounded like Terence, but then again, his crew was always up to pranks and mischief. And sometimes Terence got a hold of some really cool stuff, like dirty magazines or cigarettes. Getting excited by the thought of sneaking out, Buddy crept into the living room to check on his mother. She was still asleep, and Buddy noticed the open can of beer on the floor next to her. *Man, she never used to drink when*—but Buddy pushed that thought from his mind. He was too tough and too hard for thoughts like that.

Buddy fiddled around in his room for a while, lifting his dumbbells and listening to Metallica until it was time to leave. Then he put on his denim jacket, hiked up the collar, and walked out of the trailer. Just a short distance away, in an empty house across the railroad tracks, Kevin Miller put on his own jacket, a red windbreaker with big pockets. He put his father's gun into one of the pockets and snapped it shut. Kevin didn't bother leaving a note for his parents. They usually didn't return home from the bar until very late (and they were usually drunk), and Kevin planned on being asleep by then. He walked out of the house and made his way through the darkness to meet Buddy.

As he walked along the dirt road that would take him to the railroad tracks, Kevin was surprised to discover that he wasn't scared. Even though it was October, the month of ghosts and goblins; even though it was dark out; even though he was alone and carrying a gun in his pocket. He wasn't scared. Not anymore. Not after what he had decided he was going to do.

Buddy reached the railroad tracks and turned right. The wind was cold and stung his face. Just ahead was the canopy of trees where he and Terence would often meet to smoke cigarettes or set off cherry bombs. He wondered what Terence would have in store for him this time. He wrapped his arms around his chest, shielding himself from the cold, and turned into the wavy shadows that the canopy of trees made on the ground.

Feeling like a spy, Kevin watched from the empty train depot across the road. He saw Buddy disappear into the trees, looking tough in his denim jacket and ripped blue jeans. Kevin checked his pocket to make sure the gun was still there. He wondered if his father had ever fired it when he was in the war. Probably not. It took guts to shoot someone, even if that person was your enemy, and Kevin thought his father was

DEATH RITUALS

a gutless coward. *Just like I used to be*, Kevin thought, and he felt the gun one last time. Then he zipped up his windbreaker, walked over the train tracks, and headed into the canopy of trees.

In the darkness Buddy couldn't see much. He kicked away some empty beer cans and cigarette packs, wondering where Terence was. He tried to find the tree that he had once carved his initials into, but it was impossible. Frustrated, he sat down on a tree stump and cursed the cold. He stamped his feet against the dry leaves and blew warm air into his hands.

Just as Buddy was beginning to think Terence had played a joke on him, he heard footsteps in the darkness. He spotted a short, heavyset shadow coming toward him. But Terence was tall and skinny. For the first time Buddy felt a twinge of fear in the pit of his stomach. He got up from the tree stump.

"Who's there?" Buddy asked.

The shadow ignored him. Leaves crunched and crackled under its slow-moving feet as the shadow drew closer to Buddy.

"Answer me!" Buddy said.

The moon through the trees lit up the shadow's face. Kevin was smiling, his hand on the gun inside his pocket.

"Jesus H. Christ," exclaimed Buddy. "You tryin' to give me a heart attack, Miller? What the hell you doing out here, huh?"

"To meet you," Kevin said. He kept his hand on the gun inside his pocket, watching Buddy's every move.

The truth began to dawn on Buddy. The phone call. The phony voice trying to sound tough. He burst into laughter.

"Holy hell, Miller, that was you?" Buddy couldn't control his laughter. He hadn't stopped to think about *why* Kevin had tricked him into coming out at night; he could only think about how *stupid* Kevin looked, bundled up in his nerdy windbreaker, his hair flopping in his face over his Coke-bottle glasses.

"Stop laughing at me," Kevin said.

Buddy stopped laughing. Now he was angry. He could be at home right now, listening to music or watching the tube. Instead he was out here in the freezing cold, all because Miller had tricked him.

"Listen, blubber-guts, I'll give you five seconds to turn around and walk your fat ass outta here," Buddy threatened.

"I want to show you something, Buddy," Kevin said, tightening his hand around the gun and slowly taking it out of his pocket.

"Three seconds," Buddy warned, clenching his hands into fists.

Kevin pointed the gun at Buddy.

Buddy froze. He had seen plenty of fake guns before—those cheap, plastic ones in the toy store and on TV—and somehow he knew that the gun Kevin was holding was real. The sight of it touched something deep inside Buddy, something worse than fear, something that Buddy had refused to think about for a long time.

Buddy put up his hands.

"Please, Miller. Don't," Buddy said.

"Look at it," Kevin said. "Look at the gun." Buddy looked, his eyes on the barrel of the weapon and his stomach in knots, unsure what Miller was doing. "I don't know much about guns," Kevin continued. "I know police guns look different than soldier guns, and this is a soldier gun. It's the gun my father brought home from the war."

Buddy took a step backward. He didn't think Miller had the guts to shoot him, and he didn't understand what the jerk was blabbing on about, but Buddy wasn't taking any chances. He thought about turning around and making a break for it.

"I'm just talking to you. That's all I'm doing. Relax," Kevin said, stepping closer to Buddy and aiming the gun with a steady hand. Buddy froze once again. Kevin hesitated, an odd look on his face, and for a moment Buddy thought that he might have been crying. "Like I said, this is a soldier gun. I bet you've seen a gun like this before. You've at least read about them. I know you have."

A picture flashed through Buddy's mind right then—the image of a dark mahogany coffin and a folded American flag—but he shoved those thoughts away.

"My father was a soldier, but he never saved anyone's life. He sat behind a computer and gave orders to people. He never did a damn thing for anybody. And he's mean to me. That's why I get scared a lot—I always think he's going to beat me up." Kevin tried to control the shakiness in his voice. "My father's a coward," he said. "To use one of your words, he's a pussy."

Buddy looked at Kevin, his eyes brimming with anger.

"Shut up, Miller," he said through clenched teeth. "I mean it."

"But your father was different. He was better. Stronger. I know—I read about him in the paper," Kevin said. "I remember seeing the cars lined up, blocking traffic, and then later I heard the bagpipes playing all the way from the cemetery." As he continued to talk, Kevin lowered the gun. He knew it wasn't loaded; he had only pointed it at Buddy so that he could get his attention.

"He was shot while defending our country," Kevin said. "He was probably shot with a gun just like this one. A soldier gun. He died— he died in the war."

"You stupid fat-ass blubber-guts, I swear you better shut up!" Buddy shouted.

Tears were rolling down Kevin's cheeks; he could taste their saltiness on his lips. Normally he would be humiliated to cry in front of someone else, especially someone like Buddy, but he was done with feeling embarrassed or humiliated. He was ready to be strong.

"You probably don't remember this, but I came to your house once," Kevin said to Buddy. "Not the house where you live now, but the old house, on Trinidad Lane. We were in the third grade, and it was for your birthday party. We played video games and had ice cream cake. A few months after that, I think, your dad left for Afghanistan."

As Kevin spoke, Buddy felt his anger fade away. It was all too much to think about. He was suddenly exhausted. He sat down on the tree stump, his body shivering in the cold. Kevin put the gun back in his pocket, snapped the pocket shut, and leaned against a tree close to where Buddy was sitting.

Buddy looked at the ground. He wasn't sure if he could face Kevin. He had done so many mean things to this boy, so many mean and heartless things, all so that he could feel respected by the other guys in his crew. He had no idea what to say. He thought of his father, the war hero who died in battle, and he felt ashamed.

Kevin was also at a loss for words, but he wiped away his tears and took a deep breath. "I know you don't really hate me," he said. His feet shifted on the ground and the leaves crunched under his sneakers. "You're just angry. I'm angry too. But I don't deserve to be bullied. And you didn't deserve to have your father die."

Kevin lowered himself against the tree until he was sitting on the ground across from Buddy. "I'm sorry about the gun. It's not loaded, I swear to God. I didn't mean to scare you," he said.

Buddy shoved his hands into his pockets and looked up—not directly at Kevin, but not away from him either. "It's okay," he said.

Kevin thought for a long while about what he wanted to say next. He had never felt so calm before. So at peace with himself and the kind of kid he was—and, more importantly, the man he knew he would one day become. It was hard to find the words to fit the occasion.

"We're both victims," he said finally. "But we don't have to be. Not if we don't want to."

Buddy looked at Kevin. Buddy thought about his father again—his kindness, his compassion, and his courage. He thought of his father's portrait on the wall—the uniform so crisp and the medals so colorful and bright. He thought of his poor mother, who cried herself to sleep every night. And Buddy wondered if he and his mother had ever been crying themselves to sleep at the same time.

"What video games did we play?" Buddy asked. "I don't remember it."

"*Guitar Hero*, mostly," Kevin said. "You were really good at all those Metallica songs."

Buddy smiled. He tore at the hole in his jeans, remembering the house on Trinidad Lane. Buddy had so many happy memories from that house. Family movie nights, outdoor barbecues, throwing the football around with his dad...

Above the two boys the canopy of trees trembled in the wind. The air turned colder. It was going to start raining soon.

"You probably have to get home soon, huh?" Buddy asked after a while.

"No," Kevin answered. "Not yet."

And so they sat quietly as the wind whipped around them and a train from somewhere in the distance sounded its lonely whistle.

"Gilroy Haunted House Opens for Weekend Fundraiser" by John Bullock (originally published in *The Gilroy Press*, October, 2012, p. 1-2):

"Frankenstein's Monster House" will pry open its creaking doors for the first time this Halloween season, offering varying levels of chills that the whole family can enjoy. Located in a 125-year-old barn in the picturesque Hopper Valley, this Gilroy haunted attraction captures the ghoulish spirit of Mary Shelley's *Frankenstein*, but with a unique and kindhearted twist.

In association with property owner Barbara McCabe and the Teens Against Bullying organization, "Frankenstein's Monster House" is a two-story haunted house that depicts a playful vision of the famous mad scientist and all his creepy creations—including pneumatic monsters, coffins that open by themselves, and a robotic guard dog with glowing red eyes and dripping yellow fangs.

McCabe, who operates her antiques and collectibles establishment in the shop next to the historic barn, is more than happy to turn her property into a weekend terror zone.

"This community has given so much to me. I have a thriving business and wonderful friends," McCabe says. "Now I can give something in return, all for a worthy cause."

The spooky attraction is part of a campaign led by Teens Against Bullying, a volunteer organization started by Gilroy families, teachers, and other members of the community. Proceeds from the haunt will be donated to the program, which seeks to educate young people about bullying through school assemblies, writing contests, and community service.

"We're offering different price levels depending on how scared our visitors want to get," McCabe explains. "At dusk, children can walk through the barn with the lights on and no jump scares. They'll get to see how the animatronics work and talk to the actors. But later, after it gets dark, that's when the baddies come out—talking skeletons, howling wolves, angry villagers, and a few other surprises."

The subject of bullying resonates deeply with McCabe. The blonde 42-year-old described being a victim of such cruelty when she was a child.

"I had mild spinal curvature when I was growing up, so I had to wear a back brace every day to school," McCabe says. "The other kids laughed at me and called me hunchback. No child should have to go through something like that."

Cherie Alvarez, 15 and a sophomore at Gilroy High School, understands these words all too well. A vocal member of Teens Against Bullying, Cherie has been bullied ever since tragedy struck her family when she was 7-years-old.

"Something terrible happened, and people weren't always nice about it," Cherie says. "Like a lot of kids my age, I've been called names and I've gotten into fights. My house has been vandalized. This is why the fundraiser is so important. The goal is to bring the community together, not tear it apart."

In a grim story that will be familiar to many Gilroy residents, Cherie's mother, Gloria, was murdered in 2003 by a home intruder. While the Alvarez family has worked hard to honor the memory of the woman they loved so much, Cherie says that she has often been the target of malicious treatment as a result of the crime.

"A tabloid paper did a story on my mother's murder, with pictures and other private information, and the writer said our house was haunted," Cherie says. "Then a horror movie came out that was based on the killing. A lot of people saw the movie online, especially the kids at my middle school."

Mike Alvarez, Cherie's father, admires his daughter's courage in the face of such adversity. "After my wife died, I wanted to sell the property and move out of state, but Cherie insisted that we stay. She feels close to her mother here," says the 47-year-old father, who realized his daughter's love of Halloween when she was a small child. "She and Gloria would decorate the house for trick-or-treaters, carve pumpkins, and wear funny costumes, so this fundraiser is a tribute to the special times they shared. Halloween, haunted houses, ghost stories—Cherie takes what we fear and makes it magical."

Alvarez's painting business donated supplies to help build the haunted house, filling the open space with crumbling graves, smoking cauldrons, and a large mesh cage that holds Frankenstein's monster. "He begins the haunted house as an innocent creature with a limited understanding of his surroundings. But by the time the climax rolls around, the monster will have fully embraced his dark side," Alvarez explains with a mischievous smile. "Let's just say that cage isn't going to hold him for very long!"

To establish the tone of the haunt, Teens Against Bullying considered other Gothic works of literature for inspiration, including Bram Stoker's *Dracula* and Edgar Allan Poe's "The Tell-Tale Heart." But Coral Harrington, 15, says that Mary Shelley's *Frankenstein* was always their top choice.

"In the book, the monster is judged by his physical appearance. He's tall and scary, with strange eyes and black lips," Coral, also a sophomore at GHS, describes. "He tries to be nice and fit in with society, but he's still mistreated by the other characters. Cherie and I thought the book fit the themes of the fundraiser in an interesting way."

Both Cherie and Coral add that "Frankenstein's Monster House" avoids the novel's more violent and disturbing scenes, focusing instead on PG-13-rated scares that are suitable for most audiences.

"The only part of the book I didn't like was when the monster started killing all the people that Victor loved," Cherie says. "That's what makes the novel a tragedy. The monster's goodness becomes corrupt and evil. Our haunted house isn't *that* extreme. After all, Halloween's supposed to be fun!"

Tailored for both the faint of heart and those looking for more than a few genuine frights, "Frankenstein's Monster House" is open from dusk until midnight on Halloween weekend. Tickets will be on sale at the door. The attraction is located at Apple Dumplin' Antiques and Collectibles on Root Road.

From *Christened in Blood: Cherie Alvarez and the Apple Hill Slayings* (p. 48-50):

In addition to house-painting gigs, Michael Alvarez supported his family by taking a part-time job in the automotive department at a big-box store in San Jose, first as an auto technician, completing engine tune-ups and replacing filters. Later he was promoted to the position of the department's lead mechanic. Meanwhile, Cherie was earning good grades in high school and participating in an anti-bullying club. Donovan Keller, who taught Cherie in his World Literature class during her sophomore year, comments, "She was quiet, but given to bouts of energy and enthusiasm if the material spoke to her in a meaningful way. As a class we read *One Flew Over the Cuckoo's Nest* and *Macbeth*, and Cherie really gravitated to those. She even aced both of the exams!"

But despite her success in school and involvement in campus life, Cherie could be reticent at times, cautious of large groups of kids in fear that they might find out about her mother's murder and think she was "damaged goods"—or worse, just ignore her altogether.

"She felt more comfortable with just a few friends around who liked the same things she did," her father says today. During the next few years of high school, Mike encouraged his daughter's interests, among them music, live theater, and the poetry of William Blake, Edgar Allan Poe, and Anne Sexton. Cherie also actively took up creative writing, filling her journals with tales of bloodthirsty monsters and courageous horror-movie heroines.

"Writing helped her to deal with her mother's passing," Mike explains. "It allowed her to express her private thoughts on paper, rather than keep them bottled up inside." Cherie penned poetry and stories that contained dark and at times violent themes, including murder and suicide, but her work always ended with messages of hope and an appreciation for life.

"The emotional content of her creative writing was quite heavy for a student her age," says Keller, adding that, as a precaution, he brought some of Cherie's more alarming work to the school's guidance counselor. "Cherie always seemed to have a sensible head on her shoulders, but we live in a different time now—the 'post-Columbine' era. You can never be too careful."

Although she was a bright and inquisitive teen, Cherie struggled with bullies during her years at Gilroy High School. A few of the older kids teased her about her mother's murder, saying that the Alvarez house on Apache Court was haunted; other students either told Cherie to "get over it," or thought she was just that "moody chick" with blue steaks in her hair and a tattered copy of Poe in her back pocket.

"Sometimes, whether you want to or not, you have to fight. So there was some name-calling, some scraps and brawls after school," Mike says. "But she and her best friend, Coral, watched out for one another. I bought them both self-defense keychains, in case they ever got into serious trouble. Cherie also began working out, learning sparring techniques and other ways to defend herself."

In therapy Cherie acquired skills to grow more at ease with large groups of people and strategies to help deal with the bullying without putting herself in danger. She earned a spot on the honor roll for all but two semesters and wrote articles and movie reviews for the school newspaper. She and Coral Harrington spent a lot of their personal time composing "choose your own adventure" stories and plays, and they delighted in watching the latest wave of horror flicks like *Insidious* and the *Paranormal Activity* series.

"Her counselors and teachers worked to make school a safer place for Cherie," her father says. "At home we talked about the importance of peaceful resolution when confronting mean people and defending yourself only as a last resort."

As Cherie approached her senior year of high school, she enjoyed working at a used bookstore in Gilroy, going to the movies with Coral, and taking a writing workshop at the local library. As part of her final project for the workshop, she wrote an essay that compared a classic horror film with its modern-day remake, drawing interesting conclusions about the response to violence and embodying her peaceable view of the human condition. At the time, Cherie clearly understood that it was wrong to act out willfully and physically against others...

"Sticks, Stones, and Buckets of Blood: An Analysis of Two Carrie Whites" by Cherie Alvarez (as part of her writing workshop, Spring, 2015):

In 1976, director Brian De Palma released *Carrie*, a terrifying vision of Stephen King's epistolary novel. Presented as a stuttering young girl tormented by her peers, De Palma's Carrie White (Sissy Spacek) remains a lonely outsider throughout the film. In the opening locker room sequence, she stands alone in the shower, washing away another morning of adolescent bullying. The romantic orchestral strings and voyeuristic camera eroticize the moment as the haze of the empty shower stall offers Carrie a rare opportunity to explore her own forbidden body. But De Palma interrupts this fantasy when Carrie discovers blood running down her thighs. The haunting sounds of the locker room return, an ugly reminder that her tormentors stand just around the corner. Unaware that she is menstruating and now fearing for her life, Carrie stumbles toward her classmates, begging for help. They shove her away and pelt her with feminine hygiene products. As Miss Collins (Betty Buckley), the gym teacher, rushes to Carrie's aid, an overhead light bulb shatters, the first demonstration of Carrie's supernatural power and a foreshadowing of the film's explosive climax at the school prom.

The exploding light bulb is one of many supernatural events over which Carrie appears to have little control. In the principal's office, the ashtray falls to the floor as Carrie clutches her books; that same day, when the boy on the bicycle crashes to the ground, Carrie looks startled, clearly not understanding her telekinetic ability. De Palma couples these scenes with the sound of discordant, screeching violins, suggesting Carrie's own fear and confusion. Unlike the school bullies who delight in their physical abuse and mockery of others, Carrie takes no pleasure from the accidents or injuries that are the result of her newfound power. The vulnerability and terror that she feels at home only add to her victimization. After her Christian-fundamentalist mother (Piper Laurie) forces her to spend hours inside the prayer closet, Carrie utilizes her special talents again, cracking a mirror and opening a locked door with only the will of her mind. On both occasions Carrie shows few signs of malevolence or desire for revenge against her mother. Instead, she remains bewildered and timid, unsure how to control or define the kinetic force that surges from her subconscious.

Later, when Carrie researches telekinesis in the school library, she looks for books about miracles and human consciousness, attempting to align her supernatural ability with divine providence. As her knowledge of her talent grows, Carrie becomes more defiant of her mother, refusing to eat the apple cake at supper and insisting that she be allowed to attend the prom with Tommy Ross (William Katt). When her mother threatens to move them far away from town, the desperate teen uses her mind to slam shut the windows and the shutters. Margaret White calls her daughter a "witch," but Carrie interprets her power in far more human terms: "It's nothing to do with Satan, Momma. It's me. *Me*. If I concentrate hard enough, I can move things." Once more, Carrie uses telekinesis not to cause violence or evoke fear; she just wants to be understood, to "be a whole person before it's too late." On prom night, just before Tommy arrives at the house, Carrie and her mother have a heated argument about Carrie's decision to attend the dance. When Margaret attempts to stop Carrie from leaving her room, Carrie telekinetically hurls her mother onto the bed. In this final display of power before the blood-bath that follows, Carrie ensures that her mother remains unhurt, the soft bed breaking the woman's fall. Here, the psychic force within Carrie becomes a defense mechanism that liberates her from the psychological torment of her life at home. Ever the gentle soul, Carrie tells Margaret that she loves her before departing for the school with Tommy.

These scenes culminate in the climax at the prom, a masterwork of split-screen and slow-motion suspense. After the pig's blood splashes onto Carrie from the rafters above, she hallucinates that the entire school, including Miss Collins, is laughing at her. Defiant, Carrie willfully uses her supernatural power to close and lock all of the doors inside the gym. However, from this moment forward, the telekinetic force takes over the scene, unleashing the fire hose upon the students and causing electrical explosions. Frozen in place, her eyes stunned with terror, Carrie can only watch as a basketball backboard bursts from its hinges and plunges into Miss Collins, killing her. The death of Miss Collins remains one of the film's most visceral and telling moments. The teacher had always been kind to Carrie, comforting her in moments of distress and attempting to shield her from the cruelty of others. Her death proves that Carrie was not in control of her actions. In fact, as chaos reigns in the school gym, Carrie appears in a hypnotic trance, her body merely a host for the supernatural power within. She leaves the scene only after a fire erupts behind her and the gym goes up in flames.

As De Palma's film draws to a close, Carrie uses her telekinesis to intentionally kill others. However, a justification exists for these deaths. When Chris Hargensen (Nancy Allen) and Billy Nolan (John Travolta) flee the school grounds in Billy's car, they spot Carrie wandering on the side of the road. Careful viewers will note that it is Chris driving, and that she has every intention of running Carrie down. So when Carrie uses her power to flip the car and make it explode, it is an act of survival. Moments later, Carrie enters her house, still in her trance. Attempting to perform some ancient ritual, her mother has filled every room with lit candles. As Carrie washes the blood from her body in the bathtub, Margaret White looms wraith-like in the shadows, waiting for her chance to destroy the "witch." Usually a symbol of renewal and hope, the water awakens something painful in Carrie; she begins to sob, realizing, perhaps for the first time, the horror and humiliation of that terrible night. After dressing in a nightgown, she finds her mother and embraces her, resigning herself to a life of fundamentalist zealotry. But Margaret White has other plans. She stabs Carrie in the back with a butcher knife, and then descends upon the wounded child at the foot of the stairs. To save her life, Carrie telekinetically delivers knives, a potato peeler, and a roasting fork into her mother's body, crucifying her against the wall. As Margaret White dies, Carrie remains curled up on the floor, terrified by the deed; there is no sense of victory or vengeful smugness about her. As with the unrelenting destruction at the prom, the house begins to collapse through dark forces beyond Carrie's control. She takes her mother's body into her arms and carries her into the prayer closet, a final act of kindness before the house smothers them. In De Palma's film, the bullies remain the enemy. Carrie White, on the other hand, stays the well-principled pacifist, forced to retaliate only when backed into a corner.

In 2013, director Kimberly Peirce released her "reimagining" of *Carrie* to either neutral or negative reviews. Aside from the overwrought acting and overall lack of suspense, the film fails in its retooled characterization of Carrie White (Chloe Grace-Moretz) and the depiction of her supernatural abilities. When the fluorescent light bulb explodes during the locker room sequence, Carrie is looking directly at it, her upturned eyes brimming with secret knowledge. In the next scene, with a snarl on her face, she sends the bully on the bicycle reeling to the ground. After telekinetically shattering a mirror in the school bathroom, Carrie smiles at her newfound ability; later, in her bedroom, she levitates a pile of books, clearly in control of her power. As scenes like these continue—telekinetically, Carrie drives a knife into the floor, moves the school flag, and levitates the furniture in her home—the emphasis on her need for revenge grows. Unlike De Palma's film, in which the protagonist is depicted as a sympathetic figure unable to fully understand or control her power, Peirce's interpretation casts Carrie as the vengeful super-heroine, driven by a desire to see her tormentors hurt or killed. In one scene in Peirce's film, Carrie uses her power to lift her mother (Julianne Moore) into the air. Carrie then slams her mother onto her knees, leaving the woman sobbing on the floor. Later, Carrie telekinetically silences her mother's vocal cords, hurls her into the prayer closet, and pyrokinetically seals the door shut. The violence of these scenes functions as a prelude to the disaster at the prom, in which Peirce's Carrie, in full-blown destruction mode, unleashes a maelstrom of calculated revenge upon her classmates.

Wisely, the opening moments of Peirce's prom sequence are presented in a low-key manner, with Carrie and Tommy Ross (Ansel Elgort) gently flirting and getting to know one another. But once Chris (Portia Doubleday) and Billy (Alex Russell) dump the pig's blood onto Carrie (shown three separate times from three different angles), the tone of the sequence changes radically. As video footage of the locker room incident plays on large overhead screens for all to see, Carrie telekinetically hurls the crowd onto the floor, smashes students into glass doors, and crushes their bodies within the folding bleachers. Grunting like an animal and breathing heavily like a killer from a slasher film, she causes the gym to catch on fire and sends burning electrical cables through the air to murder her classmates. Though Carrie purposely targets the girls who bullied her in the film's opening scene, many of her innocent peers suffer and die in the collateral damage. In an attempt to garner sympathy for her heroine, Peirce does spare the gym teacher Miss Desjardin (Judy Greer) from Carrie's wrath. But the fact that Carrie has the ability to keep Miss Desjardin safe from harm is yet another example of Carrie's control over her telekinesis. Carrie could have persecuted only those who had once tormented her, but she chooses to kill almost everyone in her path instead. She is not the tenderhearted pacifist of De Palma's film, but rather an avenging "witch," a monster caked in fetid blood. With no one left to destroy, she floats in mid-air out of the gym and begins to wreak havoc throughout the town.

In Peirce's film, Carrie's roadside confrontation with Chris and Billy further demonstrates her vengeful nature. With blind hatred in her eyes, Carrie makes a conscious effort to follow Chris and Billy out of the parking lot (rather than, say, providing aid to the survivors nearby). She uses her foot to rupture the roadway, forcing Billy to turn his car around and drive toward her. As Chris orders Billy to run Carrie down, Carrie creates a telekinetic force field, bringing the car to a sudden stop and knocking Billy unconscious. Carrie then traps Chris and Billy in the vehicle, telekinetically lifts the car into the air, and hurls it into the gas pumps nearby. In the film's most violent scene, Chris's face plunges in slow-motion through the windshield, the glass cutting deeply into her skin. Carrie admires her grisly handiwork before sending a power-line crashing and exploding into the car, killing Chris and Billy. In these scenes, Carrie displays god-like supernatural strength, full control over her abilities, and malicious intent. By the time Carrie reaches her home in De Palma's film, she is an utterly tragic figure, but Peirce's Carrie remains filled with rage until the very end. When Sue Snell (Gabriella Wilde) arrives at the White residence in an effort to help, Carrie begins to wield her destructive power again. Sue begs Carrie not to hurt her, to which Carrie responds, "Why not? I've been hurt my whole life." Although she chooses not to harm Sue, these lines serve as the perfect coda for this "reimagined" Carrie, whose brief expressions of tenderness are overshadowed by the ruthless demon she has become. Peirce's film ends with Carrie allowing herself and her mother to be crushed by the falling house, paying the ultimate price for her misguided cruelty.

Brian De Palma's *Carrie* is an honest and iconic film due to its presentation of a protagonist who evokes sympathy even as fresh blood spills in her wake. In De Palma's masterpiece, Carrie's response to her emotional and physical abuse enables her to maintain her dignity as she refuses to stoop as low as those who work to destroy her. While Kimberly Peirce's *Carrie* attempts to mirror the previous version's emphasis on bullying and ritualized humiliation, the director's insistence on vindictive psychic power and bloodlust results in a cinematic misstep that turns Carrie White into just another Hollywood monster.

GILROY—During her early education, Cherie Alvarez spent many of her school days hurrying around corners, eating lunch behind the gym, or hiding out in one of the classrooms.

Cherie created a map of her school in her mind, determining which hallways were safe, the best time to grab her books from her locker, and where she would meet up with her friends.

She often wore a fleece sweatshirt to school because she found it easy to hide her face inside its oversized hood. She wore purple running sneakers in case she had to make a quick getaway.

"Certain areas of the school were off limits to me, like the courtyard behind the science wing or the benches near the basketball hoops. You learn who's going to be where, and then you avoid those people who will start trouble," Cherie said.

Beginning in the first grade—when a shocking tragedy turned her house into a place of grief, sadness, and ugly rumor—Cherie said she was picked on by her peers, many of whom found the subjects of murder and death "funny."

"The court proceedings lasted a few years, and then came the true-crime books and direct-to-cable horror movies. It just never stopped, year after year," Cherie, now 17, said. "It was an endless cycle that gave bullies all the ammunition they needed."

In 2003, when Cherie was 7-years-old, her mother was beaten to death in one of the most violent murders the town of Gilroy has ever seen. That Gloria Alvarez was 16-weeks pregnant at the time of her death only added to the unspeakable crime. "My mom was excited to bring my new brother or sister into the world," said Cherie. "The whole family was."

But instead of providing understanding and support, some of Cherie's classmates delighted in making up stories and schoolyard rhymes about the murder. As Cherie got older, the escalating taunts and smears turned physical. "I've gotten into my share of fights," she said with a rueful laugh. "But I'm strong. I'm in shape and I know how to throw a mean left hook."

To survive school and confront her obstacles head-on, Cherie rallied with her friends to come up with an action plan. Together they formed an anti-bullying coalition and arranged community events to raise awareness about the importance of treating others with respect and kindness.

"When you're a kid, no one tells you the world is full of cruel and random acts. And no one tells you that people will intentionally set out to hurt you," said Cherie. "I think that's why I read so many books about kids who are ostracized and watch movies like *Carrie* and *Prom Night*. They remind me that I'm not alone."

Cherie contributes her gentle spirit to her parents, who taught her to never make fun of others and forgive those who do harm.

"My father raised me to defend myself if necessary," she said. "But I also understand that there are usually victims on both sides, and forgiveness allows us to cut the ropes that tie us to bad experiences."

Cherie graduated from Gilroy High School last week as one of the hand-selected students to deliver a speech during the graduation ceremony. With approval from school administration, she addressed her family tragedy and the bullies who tried to make her life miserable.

"They say words can never hurt you, but they do. Sometimes they are more powerful than a fist, more painful than being shoved to the ground or getting punched in the stomach. But none of us is perfect. Like everyone here, I'm still learning how to be good. I'm still learning how to live with grief and still be the best person I can be," she spoke before the crowd of students, parents, and faculty.

In the fall, Cherie will attend San Jose State University, where she plans to major in psychology and minor in film and theater studies. She is the first person in her immediate family to attend college, a fact that makes her father proud.

"She'll be close enough to home if she ever needs me, but she's ready to be on her own," Mr. Alvarez said.

Many people have told Cherie that college will be a safer and more enriching experience than high school—and it is that kind of encouragement that gives her the strength to overcome the troubles of her past and embrace her future.

"I don't want to hold myself back," she said. "I want to write. I want to be creative. I want to have a voice in the world."

"Inside America's Top 10 Extreme Haunted Houses" by Adam Lee Sargent (originally published in *Haunted America*, October, 2014, p. 7-9):

Kidnappings. Bondage. Psychological humiliation. Torture and murder. Featuring all of these ghastly scenarios and more, extreme haunts have recently developed into a startling new trend of Halloween entertainment. With top-quality gore and terrifying scenes that test the boundary between simulation and reality, these haunted houses cast participants in hardcore tales of graphic violence, perverse sexuality, and grotesqueries of the darkest kind. In freewheeling towns like Los Angeles and San Francisco, extreme haunts have already established a sturdy foothold. But, as the spooky season draws near, it might surprise you to learn that these nightmarish caverns of horror are popping up all over the country. Join *Haunted America* as we bravely lift the funeral veil on 10 of America's scariest, freakiest, most insane scream houses!

10. Feargrounds of Hell

Where: Salt Lake City, Utah

Age restrictions: Parental advisory for extreme violence, hallucinatory imagery, and mature subject matter

Features: Demonic and religious themes, minor physical contact, strobe lights, group separation, narrow passageways

Satanic horror clashes with picturesque Salt Lake City in "Feargrounds of Hell," located at a real farm on the outskirts of town. Championed by Halloween fanatics as the only full-contact haunted attraction in the state, this partially outdoor experience involves a corn maze, a haunted grain silo, and a centuries-old barn where satanic ceremonies allegedly took place. Real-life protestors are often seen (and heard) outside the fence that surrounds the farm, but their puritanical cries have failed to stop the hundreds of guests each year who hope their time in the haunt will lead to an encounter with the deranged Dr. Theodore Brule, an evil surgeon who enjoys separating guests from their group and "abducting" them to his subterranean medical lab.

9. The Underground
Where: San Francisco, California
Age restrictions: Adults 18+ only
Features: Sensory deprivation, confinement, extreme darkness, simulated live burial, physical contact, verbal taunting, all guests must sign waiver

A wickedly intense burial simulation, "The Underground" is part of a much larger haunted attraction called "The Haunted Mansion of Terror," located near San Francisco's Golden Gate Park. If you've ever fantasized about your own funeral, now is your chance to get sealed inside a real coffin and face your mortal coil. But what really makes this attraction extreme is its perverted host, a masked giant with skull gauges and pierced nips. Known as the Crypt-Keeper, this leather-bound lunatic likes nothing more than to grope and humiliate you before sending you off to your dirt nap.

8. The Haunted Woods of Roberts Mill Road
Where: London, Ohio
Age restrictions: Parental advisory for explicit content and adult subject matter
Features: Abduction scenarios, survival horror themes, intense physical contact, aberrant criminal activity, confinement

The woods at the edge of Roberts Mill Road are rumored to be haunted by the ghost of an old woman that wanders among the trees and decrepit cabins that stand just off the roadside. The producers of "The Haunted Woods of Roberts Mills Road" capitalize on this urban legend, filling their haunt with all sorts of evil spirits, including wendigos, skinwalkers, and jersey devils. But the haunt's most threatening terrors come in the form of deformed mountain men dressed in filthy overalls and carrying pitchforks and pocketknives. The actors in this haunt have been known to stage "kidnap" scenarios with some of their guests, binding them with rope, smearing their faces with fish guts to attract bears, and leaving them deserted in the woods. A sign nailed to a tree outside the haunt warns that some of the actors are actually "escaped convicts" from a nearby correctional institution.

7. Alien Infection

Where: Glen Mills, Pennsylvania

Age Restrictions: Parental advisory for mature content and simulated violence

Features: Sexual situations, heavy physical contact, verbal abuse, nudity, flashing lights, food and water ingestion, all guests must sign waiver

Started in 2012, "Alien Infection" puts a smutty spin on the haunted house archetype. As guests wait in line, a bank of video monitors shows a UFO crash landing. Scaly, sore-encrusted aliens emerge from the ship onscreen just as real air raid sirens and flashing lights barrage and disorient the patrons. Men in black sunglasses and suits disrupt the queue, dragging guests into a small building designed to look like some shady medical research center. Once inside, guests are treated to an endless spectacle of revolting sci-fi horror, including fornicating space creatures, an alien birth, diseased mutants, and a cafeteria scene involving giant beetles and a buttery substance that tastes like spoiled sour cream.

6. Lights Off

Where: Los Angeles, California

Age restrictions: Parental advisory for simulated peril and multiple scary situations and images

Features: Demonic themes, physical contact, strobe lights, pitch darkness, claustrophobic situations

Set inside a 100-year-old playhouse in downtown Los Angeles, "Lights Off" is one of the more unusual extreme haunts on this list, billing itself as interactive theater, a haunted house, and a psychedelic art installation all in one. As part of the compelling storyline, guests attend a premier art show hosted by the Poison Affair, a mysterious group of benefactors that has amassed a collection of paintings with supposedly hypnotic powers. Led by tour guides dressed in horned masks and colorful robes, patrons walk the gallery and listen to sordid tales of black masses, ancient spells, and satanic cults. But when the lights go out, what supernatural forces will rise from the deviant artwork? And who will be the guest of honor? An immersive, intense, and even educational experience, "Lights Off" is a collaborative effort made possible by some of the most creative minds in the haunt industry today.

5. The Devil's Business: Manson's House of Blood
Where: Los Angeles, California
Age restrictions: Adults 18+ only
Features: Must enter only in pairs, simulated violence and torture, graphic depictions of bloodshed, extreme physical contact, semi-nudity, loud noises, confinement, all guests must sign waiver

Focusing on an infamous true crime, "The Devil's Business: Manson's House of Blood" attempts to recreate that grisly scene from 10050 Cielo Drive, where Charles Manson's gang of murderous misfits killed actress Sharon Tate (who was over eight months pregnant at the time) and her friends. Our experience with the haunt, which takes place in a creepy old house off Mulholland Drive in Los Angeles, included simulated stabbings and suffocation, being bound and gagged, scenes of dead bodies and gore-soaked furniture, and an auditory assault of human screams, crying babies, distorted music, and gunshots.

4. Execution
Where: New York/Los Angeles
Age restrictions: Parental advisory for simulated torture and executions
Features: Simulated violence, intense physical contact, graphic depictions of simulated death, electric shock, submersion in water, restraints, guests may be separated, all guests must sign waiver

Coming in at an impressive #4 on our list, "Execution" features some of the more traditional aspects of haunted houses, including a walkthrough format, mandatory "jump scares," and actors in ghoulish face-paint and prosthetics. But what makes this extreme haunt so disturbing is its bleak subject matter. Guests are guided through a sort of torture museum, where each showcase displays a different kind of execution. From the guillotine to the electric chair, from simulated lethal injections to the firing squad, it's all here in gory, FX-heavy detail. In more recent years, "Execution" has gone the immersive horror theater route, whereby executioners in black masks subject guests to their own "executions" and torture sequences, including the use of minor electric shock and faux-waterboarding. Morbidly fascinating and not for the squeamish, "Execution" is worth the price of admission for the incredible animatronics, cool special effects, and brooding atmosphere.

3. Marsha's Schoolhouse of Terror
Where: Atlanta, Georgia
Age restrictions: Adults 18+ only
Features: Extreme violence and gore, religious themes, intense physical contact, food and water ingestion, psychosexual role-play, electric shock, blood play, use of safe word, all guests must sign waiver

An uncensored and manic descent into your worst schoolhouse memories, "Marsha's Schoolhouse of Terror" plays out like an X-rated horror movie. Filled with satanic teachers, lecherous priests, lusty nuns, and undead teenage bullies, this haunt will put your psychological limits to the test. Apparently, not every customer gets to meet the ax-wielding matron herself, Marsha Devereaux—but if you do, be forewarned. Online reports indicate that the voluptuous headmistress enjoys rough physical contact, gross-tasting edibles, electric shock, and minor bloodletting. And if all that weren't terrifying enough, the haunt is held inside a real abandoned schoolhouse in northern Atlanta.

2. Death Wish

Where: Pontiac, Michigan

Age restrictions: Adults 18+ only

Features: Violence, physical contact, confinement, high-action sequences, abduction scenarios, sensory deprivation, all guests must sign waiver

With its name borrowed from street justice films, this controversial attraction allows patrons to channel their inner Charles Bronson and kick some butt. But while you can shoot at your assailants with marshmallow bazookas and wiffle-ball launchers, and "attack" them with padded weapons, be careful—at any time the tables can be turned and you might find yourself on the receiving end of a tactical baton or riddled by soft beanbag rounds. Each Halloween season "Death Wish" changes its theme, offering up unique locations (a cemetery, an abandoned doll-making factory, a mock prison) where you can transform into a vigilante warrior. With gun massacres on the rise throughout the world, we have to call into question the ethicality of an attraction that requires its participants to commit violent acts against each other, however simulated those acts might be. And yet that's nothing compared to the attraction that squeaked in at our #1 spot...

1. The World of Horrors

Where: Marietta, Ohio

Age restrictions: Adults 21+ only

Features: Extreme violence, simulated acts of murder, intense physical contact, use of blank-firing guns and other pneumatic weapons, hostage scenarios, darkness and confinement, pyrotechnics, all guests must sign waiver

This year's installment of "The World of Horrors" hasn't officially opened yet, but this large-scale, multi-haunt has already captured the country's attention with an ambitious online marketing campaign involving interactive websites, newsletters, and magazine cover stories—and if the rumors are true, one of the attractions on the grounds this year will be loosely based on the making of a fictional snuff film. With over 40 acres of haunt space—including a creepy warehouse, a parking lot maze, and an exploitation video store—the attraction hopes to lure those who are looking for the "ultimate hardcore killing experience." Promising original scenes, dedicated actors, and authentic props, "The World of Horrors" could be the next big thing in the expanding universe of extreme haunts, but have the producers gone too far? When does Halloween entertainment become exploitative trash? Only time will tell as "The World of Horrors" sets to fling open its blood-streaked doors in a matter of weeks. Murder has never looked so much fun...

"Ohio's Unapologetic Nightmare" by Lance Berryman (originally published in *Haunters Monthly*, October, 2014, pg. 3-5):

From a spooky backyard cemetery to one of the largest and most controversial haunted houses in the country, "The World of Horrors" has melded horror films and stories of true crime to consistently modify its product for an ever-changing market. For the past several years, their team has stunned and shocked audiences with dynamic sets and gore-heavy special effects, and in 2009 the attraction was voted Southeast Ohio's most popular haunted house. For the upcoming Halloween season, "The World of Horrors" has descended into the deepest, darkest, and most psychologically terrifying dens of hell to deliver a truly visceral experience for all of its courageous guests.

"The World of Horrors" began over two decades ago when owner Roscoe "Ross" Cahill was just 26-years-old. A lifelong horror fan and monster-truck enthusiast, Ross had always been interested in haunted attractions, building his first haunted house in his backyard when he was in his early teens. Inspired by *Tales from the Crypt* comics and slasher films like *Black Christmas* and *Halloween*, Ross developed a passion for designing stark but terrifying sets and writing pulse-pounding storylines to parallel the scares.

After the moderate success of his backyard haunts, Ross decided to build a larger, more complex attraction that would lure big crowds and draw media attention unlike ever before. In the summer of 1993, he moved into a new house in Marietta and began constructing an elaborate 5,000 square-foot attraction that started in his living room, wound its way through the back of the house, and then spilled into his huge backyard for a blood-soaked climax. "That first big haunt was a labor of love," says Ross with a chuckle. "I spent weeks tearing down walls, pulling up floorboards, and studying all my favorite comics and horror movies to get ideas. I enlisted the help of my friends and family, and as time went on, the haunt really started to come together."

Much to Ross's amusement today, the first installment of "The World of Horrors" almost didn't happen. He and his team were still scrambling to put the finishing touches on the haunt even as a small crowd of patrons was gathering outside. "Our actors were adjusting their costumes, fixing their make-up, all at the last minute. We were still testing electrical outlets when the doors opened," remembers Ross. "But when I heard the first customer scream, I knew our hard work had paid off and it was all worth it."

On that fateful Halloween night, "The World of Horrors" attracted nearly 100 visitors, forcing police to arrive and shut down the event. Ross spent the rest of that evening gathering props, sweeping up debris, and weighing his next move. If "The World of Horrors" generated this much buzz in a residential neighborhood and with limited advertising, he thought, imagine the endless possibilities of expanding the space and reaching a wider audience. It was at that moment that Ross decided he would search for a new location and open a commercial haunted attraction in October of the following year.

Today, Ross explains that it was not only his interest in horror and his love of scaring people that helped "The World of Horrors" grow and prosper. In what he describes as an existential moment, the young entrepreneur saw what he called a "cruel darkness" in the world—and it troubled him deeply. "There was Richard Ramirez, the serial killer who made his victims swear to Satan before he raped and murdered them. Then, a few years later, Jeffrey Dahmer, the Milwaukee Cannibal, his apartment crammed with human bones and rotting corpses. Then the Green River Killer, the Cleveland Strangler—just headline after headline of death and slaughter," Ross says. "These stories disturbed me, and I saw only one way to vent my fear and anger. I turned true crime into a new kind of Halloween horror. I began focusing on graphic realism in every set I designed." Ross's dedication to providing intense, physical scares and his interest in real-life murder stories have since thrilled and terrified thousands of people, but they have also made him the subject of much scrutiny and moral outrage. "I'm not very popular in some circles of the industry," he concedes. "I'm well aware of that."

"The World of Horrors" is now located in a 50,000 square-foot retail location and houses some of the most jaw-dropping and frightening sets ever to appear in a haunted attraction. However, the road to such a prime piece of real estate was a rough one. As Ross expanded his haunt—adding more actors, practical and digital effects, and narratives torn from sordid tabloid headlines —the attraction moved from location to location and failed to develop a loyal following. Ross comments, "I was very ambitious and I had a dedicated team working behind me, but I needed help in every department—cash flow, construction, hiring, management. And as the haunt grew so did the competition. I was getting in over my head."

A burst of new creativity and energy came in 2011 when 33-year-old Bobby Pruitt visited the haunt as a guest. A set designer and fiction writer, Bobby saw great potential in "The World of Horrors" and felt confident that he could contribute in a meaningful way. "It was a quality production, but I didn't feel there were enough legitimate scares," Bobby says. "I had a ton of notes and sketches in my journals, so I called up Roscoe and arranged to see him." By this time, Bobby had been helping to design attractions for several neighborhood haunts throughout central Ohio. When he wasn't writing horror stories or making performance art with his girlfriend, he was working on haunted houses, cobbling together the disturbing themes of exploitation cinema with his own twisted ideas of what scares people to their core. "I imagined a haunted house that preyed upon our worst fears. Fears so real that you can feel, smell, and *taste* them," Bobby explains. "A haunted house that showed just how ugly and unforgiving society can be."

A unique partnership was born. Bobby took over duties as lead set designer while Ross continued to raise enough money to terrify his audience. "The World of Horrors" began featuring massive scenes, interactive environments, and actors fully immersed in their roles. But it is the latest addition to the haunted attraction that has drawn the ire of protest groups throughout the country and given the haunt a polarizing reputation: for the upcoming Halloween season, one of the attractions inside "The World of Horrors" will be centered on the making of a fictional snuff film.

"It's never been done before," says Ross, his voice tinged with both bravado and nervousness. "The concept, the money needed, the moral implications—it's a big risk to take."

To highlight this shocking addition, Ross and Bobby have crafted one of the most clever haunt entrances ever conceived. The box office to this attraction is set inside a crumbling video store, where the clerks are murdered ghouls and the shelves are filled with mock-up videotapes of exploitation classics like *Faces of Death*, *Cannibal Holocaust*, and *Nekromantik*. As customers buy their tickets, footage of televised suicides, martyrdom videos, and real beheadings play on computer monitors overhead. Aware that his attraction has entered "extreme" territory, Ross describes the critical thinking that went into the controversial experience: "This is an event unlike anything in the haunt industry right now. Whether or not you believe that snuff films exist, we give you the chance to witness a depiction of one of the most notorious and vile scenarios ever imagined in the world of true crime. As a participant, you will get to select the victim. You will get to choose the method of her death. You will get to choose her executioner from a cast of wild characters. And best of all—each murder sequence will be filmed and placed on a special website for our guests to watch later."

If all goes according to plan, this October's "The World of Horrors" will feature four attractions in one enormous retail space. The snuff haunt, tentatively titled "Blood Orgy," will be interactive and fast-paced, but guests must be over the age of 18 and adhere to a strict set of rules. "Without question there's going to be a waiver of liability for 'Blood Orgy,'" Ross says. "It's a very physical, gruesome, and intense experience. Bobby has found some actors—I don't know where he found these guys—who are fully committed to causing mayhem and terror. It's going to be totally insane."

Totally insane—that is, if "Blood Orgy" is allowed to open in the first place. Currently, the proposed haunt has attracted intense criticism from victim advocacy groups and other organizations that find the premise unethical and exploitative. But Bobby Pruitt refuses to even consider the complaints and negative publicity. "Everyone hurts. Everyone is in pain. I want to take people into the black hole of their suffering and show them desires they don't even know they have—even if I have to break them to do it," he says, adding that he has invested countless hours detailing the environment of "Blood Orgy" and training the actors how to perform like true maniacs during the haunt. "I push forward because I believe in the finished product. I believe there's a market for it. People only do what they want to do—and they want to be pushed beyond their limits."

Promotional material for "Blood Orgy"

MARIETTA, OHIO—The owner of a Southeast Ohio haunted attraction revealed last week that he had planned to replicate a snuff film in his latest production, giving guests the opportunity to participate in the simulated murder of a teenage girl.

Victim advocacy groups criticized the haunted attraction's owner for exploiting underage women and for celebrating violence and sexual abuse. The majority of the protests reached the point of vilification, with many groups calling for a complete closure of the production and urging authorities to investigate the company's business practices.

As soon as the company, known as "The World of Horrors," publicized its press release, petitions began appearing online to prevent the attraction from opening in October. Thousands of people signed the petitions, with many describing the plans for the haunted house as "unethical," "cruel," and "sick."

Part of the press release for "The World of Horrors" read: "They come in the dark. They come with knives and rope. They take young girls for their own, subjecting them to humiliating and perverted acts. And as virgin blood spills, every drop is captured on film for the world to enjoy. Welcome to the most debauched Halloween event Ohio has ever seen: Blood Orgy."

Lynn Chelton, who created one of the online petitions, worked tirelessly to prevent "The World of Horrors" from opening its "snuff" house. "I didn't have a problem with their other attractions, but this one treated violence against women carelessly and without ethical thought," she said. "I also heard rumors about illegal hiring practices and inadequate training of employees, which had me equally concerned."

After learning about the online petitions and meeting with representatives from advocacy groups in Ohio, the owner of "The World of Horrors," Roscoe Cahill, decided to remove the snuff-film simulation from his menu of haunted attractions.

"The line between entertainment and the exploitation of real-life crime victims has become much thinner in recent years," Cahill said in a written statement. "I have made a decision to move my attractions away from extreme themes and return to the kinds of haunted houses that everyone can enjoy."

Though the majority of those involved with this story support Cahill's decision, one of his business partners, Bobby Pruitt, has quit the company as a result. The lead scenic designer on "The World of Horrors," Pruitt sees no problem with haunted attractions that depict victims, especially young women, in situations of sexualized violence, including rape and "snuff"—a film made for financial gain that purportedly shows a person actually being murdered.

"Sex, women, blood, and death are all united in the animal side of our lives. And that's what this attraction was going to be about—the eroticism of a young girl's murder, the darkest reality of our existence," Pruitt said. He insisted that no one would have actually been harmed during "Blood Orgy," including the female performers portraying the "snuff" victims.

"We are pleased with Mr. Cahill's decision to replace the production with something more suitable and respectful," said Chelton, who now plans to investigate other haunted attractions that may be promoting similar values throughout the country.

"Not Your Average Haunted House: *The Satanist* Comes to San Jose State" by Felicia Ryan (originally published in *The San Jose Spartan*, October, 2015, p. 2-3):

Something fiercely original is creeping its way to the Audrey Hall Theater this Halloween season, bringing with it elements of *Rosemary's Baby*, radio drama, and improvisational theater. Rumors have been circulating around campus that it's the most terrifying show the theater department has ever produced, and students have reported having strange and even paranormal experiences during rehearsals. Part of the mystery stems from the transformation of the theater itself, with all the plush seats covered in velvet purple cloth and candelabras lighting an eerie path to the small stage. A tale of satanic savagery and wicked humor has descended upon our school's little theater, and your Halloween just might never be the same.

Written by freshmen students Cherie Alvarez and Coral Harrington as part of their playwriting class, *The Satanist* represents a new trend in performance art: a combination of haunted-attraction aesthetics and immersive theater. In September, Alvarez and Harrington's script was selected by their peers to be work-shopped and produced as one of San Jose State's more intimate fall productions. Part of the show's allure is that the audience for each performance is limited to only ten guests, each of whom will sit in chairs close to the stage and become an interactive part of the show. Audience members will be encouraged to explore the whimsical sets during the performance—opening drawers, flipping through books, studying artwork, and discovering vital clues to the story's mystery—all while talking to and working with the actors. The audience must also understand when to sit back and let the action unfold around them, but the play contains various cues that tell them what to do and when.

Though the Audrey Hall Theater stage is fairly small, the Gothic details of the play's settings—an isolated mountain estate and a barren graveyard—reflect the morbidly funny and at times frightening narrative. The actors in *The Satanist* will wander freely throughout the stage and among the audience, inviting them to play an active role in many of the scenes. In this way, the audience helps to bring *The Satanist* to life, uncovering props that are critical to the story. But Alvarez is quick to note that participating in the play as an audience member is an entirely safe and entertaining experience. "Some Halloween attractions are intensely physical and graphic, forcing their guests to act out horrible scenarios, like simulated murder," she says, referring to a recent story out of Ohio about a haunted house centered on the making of a snuff film. "What we're trying to do with *The Satanist* is combine our love of haunted houses and interactive theater, but without hurting anyone."

Though interactive theater is not new, it's definitely not the norm either, and the creative team behind the production has gone to great lengths to make such an undertaking work for the audience and the performers. Katie Morrison, the director of the show, spoke with *The San Jose Spartan* about the initial reactions to the play when it was first work-shopped with students from the theater department. Morrison described the difficulty the actors had in interacting with the mock audience, ad-libbing lines to keep the drama moving and trying to anticipate what an audience member might do or say in the moment. The director addressed the risk that interactive theater poses, as patrons might not always respect the vulnerability of the actors or the narrative itself. "Hopefully, a certain kind of theater-goer purchases a ticket to this show. Someone open-minded and creative who understands the importance of going with the flow and having fun," Morrison says. "We rehearsed for weeks and acted out countless scenarios of what could go wrong, and now we're ready to present something that's never been done on our college campus before."

The Satanist, which tells the story of a lonely woman whose husband may belong to a murderous cult, promises to deliver a fun and intoxicating slice of experimental theater to San Jose State. Co-writer Harrington explains, "It's a haunted house and a stage play merged into one, but you're not forced to do anything against your will.

However, we do recommend that you wear comfortable shoes and clothes that you don't mind getting a little wet!"

The Satanist premieres Halloween weekend, with two shows a night running Thursday through Saturday. Showtimes are at 7 and 9:30, and audiences are encouraged to arrive early to explore the lobby and conjoining rooms, all of which are decorated with macabre themes. Check back with *The San Jose Spartan* next week, as our special Halloween edition will feature interviews with the cast and crew of the show.

"The Power of Three: The Talented Women Behind *The Satanist*" by Clement Curtis (originally published in *San Jose Discovery*, October, 2015, p. 2-4):

Take one step into the Audrey Hall Theater at San Jose State University this Halloween weekend and you'll find yourself immersed in a world straight out of Edgar Allan Poe and the suspense radio melodramas of yesteryear. Roam an insane woman's estate, wander a crumbling cemetery, interact with characters, and help discover their dark secrets. Though performed on a small stage, *The Satanist* will guide audiences through a bleak landscape of shattered dreams and devilish schemes, all while asking that the guests take part in the ensuing action. The play features only two sets but they are remarkably detailed, full of womb-like shadows and supernatural lights. The limited-run performance also makes clever use of its many ghoulish props, some of which are hidden in plain sight while others are tucked away into cobwebbed corners of the stage that the audience must explore in order to advance the plot.

After sitting through an intense rehearsal, I spoke with the writers of *The Satanist*, SJSU freshmen Cherie Alvarez and Coral Harrington, as well as junior Paula Green, who plays the lead female role in the play, to learn about the challenges of interactive theater, their motivations behind the project, and their interest in treating the horror genre and its fans with dignity and respect.

SAN JOSE DISCOVERY: Prior to your work on *The Satanist*, had you worked in theater before?

CHERIE ALVAREZ: I've always been drawn to the performing arts, but more as a creative writer and set designer than as an actress. In high school, Coral and I helped design several different haunted houses as part of an anti-bullying campaign. And I've always connected with the horror genre, not only for its dark and moody style but also for its many psychological layers. Horror fiction can teach us about ourselves and highlight strengths we never knew we had.

PAULA GREEN: I was a dancer in high school, but I didn't start getting into acting until I came to SJSU as a freshman. Last summer I was an understudy for a musical revue in San Francisco that had some Gothic elements and from there I started reading authors like Poe and Lovecraft and Algernon Blackwood. So when Cherie and Coral presented *The Satanist* in our writing class, I responded deeply to the material and felt I had an understanding of where they were trying to go with the script. Soon after that I auditioned and got the part of Caroline Forsythe, which is the lead role.

CORAL HARRINGTON: I've always written horror stories, poems, and plays, even when I was a little kid. My parents were worried about me because I kept bringing monster magazines to school and writing stories where all the adults would get murdered and only the little kids and animals would survive! I also love haunted houses and the narratives that come with them. My favorite is the story of Master Gracey and Madame Leota from Disneyland's Haunted Mansion, which has elements of comedy and melodrama, but is actually quite disturbing. We tried to bring our love of all these types of spooky entertainment into *The Satanist*.

SAN JOSE DISCOVERY: *The Satanist* seems to merge many different genres into one, including haunted attractions and interactive theater. How would you describe the play?

ALVAREZ: In one way, the play functions like a traditional haunted house, with guests walking through a stationary set and reacting to the environment. The special effects and the props were certainly influenced by the haunted attractions you see during Halloween. But we also wanted to create a standard theater show—something along the lines of Tim Kelly's *The Uninvited* or Ira Levin's *Veronica's Room*. Sometimes the audience remains seated and watches the drama, but other times they stand up and play a direct role in the story.

SAN JOSE DISCOVERY: The two sets in *The Satanist* are perfectly suited for the small space, but still allow the audience members to walk around freely and explore. Because of the interactive nature of the play, how are the sets and props utilized differently than in a more traditional stage show?

ALVAREZ: Once the sets were finished, Katie Morrison, our director, allowed the cast and crew to wander through them and discover some of their "secrets" on our own. The sets are very much like a haunted house in that way. As we explored and poked around, we *became* the audience, which enabled us to fine-tune the script based on how we think they're going to respond.

GREEN: The main set, the living room at the Forsythe estate, has a ton of props that may or may not get used during each performance. A few are essential to the plot and we work them in no matter what, but the importance of some of the props depends on the value the audience gives to any given object. It takes a certain kind of person to really enjoy all that *The Satanist* has to offer. You have to be willing to step outside your comfort zone and interact with the performers and the sets themselves. Our hope is that our guests will work with us— like the unspoken agreement between a magician and his audience. The audience members become characters themselves and hold a stake in the final outcome of the story.

SAN JOSE DISCOVERY: Paula, you've been a featured dancer in San Francisco and performed in classics like *Othello* and *One Flew Over the Cuckoo's Nest*, but *The Satanist* seems far removed from your past work. How do you prepare for a role in which the unexpected could happen onstage at any time?

GREEN: Fortunately, we work-shopped the play in and out of class, even bringing in a small student audience to get their input and interact with them onstage. With dancing, I never think about the audience; I'm too consumed with my movements, balance, and timing. But *The Satanist* blends the audience and the actor into one. We feed off their energy in order to put on the most entertaining performance. We want the audience to have fun. So I watch their gestures and mannerisms, their behavior during the show. That will tell me how to play off the audience when the time comes. *The Satanist* is an immersive experience that brings observers into the action, but they won't be forced to do anything or be put through any major physical challenges during the performance.

SAN JOSE DISCOVERY: It sounds like maintaining the safety of your audience is a crucial part of the show as a whole. Cherie and Coral, I've read that your script of *The Satanist* was a direct response to extreme haunted houses that are notoriously cruel or physically rough with their customers. Is that true?

ALVAREZ: It's partially true. I understand that people who love Halloween and horror movies are always looking for the next big thing, the next big scare. It's like how I felt with the first *Paranormal Activity* movie. It terrified me, and it re-energized the genre with new ideas and techniques for scaring people. But can a film or a haunted attraction go too far? Some haunted houses stage kidnapping scenarios and murder simulations, and "The World of Horrors" just got shut down due to major protests. Living out your own horror movie sounds exciting, and people over the age of 18 are allowed to do what they want—we just don't think you should be held against your will, abused, or humiliated in any way.

HARRINGTON: I've seen videos from haunted houses like "Alien Infection" and "Marsha's Schoolhouse of Terror," and it's the sexual violence that crosses the line for me. In real life, people are assaulted in their homes. They are kidnapped and raped and murdered. It's bad enough that tabloids and gore websites exploit these kinds of stories, but now extreme haunted houses are getting in on the game. And who's signing up for legalized torture and simulated sexual assault? Not trauma survivors. Not rape victims. So the only people who are participating in these types of attractions are the ones who have never experienced it themselves in real life. Cherie and I love haunted houses and we're always going to be interested in the latest trends in Halloween entertainment. We admire the creativity and the passion for the product, but artists should think about the consequences of their work. *The Satanist* has its share of blood and horror, but it's also over the top and goofy. We were conscientious of the real-life victims of abuse and murder as we wrote it, so it plays more like a *Tales from the Crypt* episode than it does a simulated torture house.

SAN JOSE DISCOVERY: Paula, you have a challenging task when performing onstage. While remembering your lines and staying in character, you also have to select members from the audience to help you discover clues and other items that your character needs to survive in the story. Do you choose them at random or do you seek out certain types of people?

GREEN: *The Satanist* is the most intimate show I've done. I'm right next to the audience— taking their hands, talking to them, asking them for help. I tend to zero in on the people who make direct eye contact. That tells me that we're on the same page and they're ready to get involved and have some fun. I try to gauge a person's comfort level and then go from there.

SAN JOSE DISCOVERY: Judging from past theater shows at San Jose State, *The Satanist* is one of the most experimental attempts at visual and performing arts that the university has ever made. If interactive productions like this continue, how do you take horror theater in new directions without crossing that ethical line we discussed earlier?

ALVAREZ: One way to achieve that goal would be to avoid fictional narratives that force the participants to relinquish total control to the people or "characters" in charge. Falling victim to a horde of flesh-eating zombies is one thing; acting out gang-rape or abduction scenarios is entirely another. By getting the audience involved physically and emotionally, interactive theater and extreme haunted houses can send out dangerous and abusive messages about personal relationships, sexual practices, and other important issues.

HARRINGTON: If it's a full-contact haunt or a heavily interactive piece, the performers need to be well-trained and understand the dynamic of the audience they're working with. Now, allegedly, "The World of Horrors" hired a crew of ex-cons to work their attraction. I don't know what kind of training they had, I don't know if the actors had a history of real-life violence or assault, and that makes me nervous for the people who were planning to attend. Whether it's a performance of *The Satanist* or an interactive haunted house, the scenes need to look violent, not *be* violent. And there should never be violence, real or simulated, at the cost of human dignity.

The Satanist: By Cherie Alvarez and Coral Harrington. Directed by Katie Morrison. Starring Paula Green, Chris Lassiter, Sheryl Manning, and Jefferson Walker. 7 p.m. and 9:30 p.m. Thursday-Saturday, October 29-31; 1 hour and 30 minutes; no intermission. $35. Audrey Hall Theater Stage, San Jose State University.

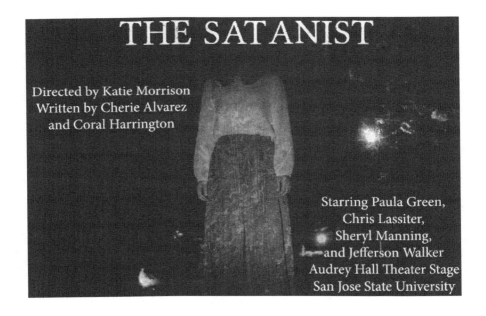

THE SATANIST

Directed by Katie Morrison
Written by Cherie Alvarez
and Coral Harrington

Starring Paula Green,
Chris Lassiter,
Sheryl Manning,
and Jefferson Walker
Audrey Hall Theater Stage
San Jose State University

THE SATANIST

ACT I

Setting: *A living room at Summit Drive, a large house tucked away on the seaside. The room is dark, the walls sheer black. The various ornamentations— including wall sconces, framed portraits, and a revolver behind a glass case—are all shades of black and gray.*

Far stage right is a front door that opens to the living room. On the wall next to the door are several keys hanging on hooks. A pair of galoshes, caked with dried mud, sits beneath a foyer table near the door.

Stage right is an open doorway that leads to a stairwell. On the wall near the doorway hangs a coat rack made out of deer antlers. A black cloak hangs from one of the antlers. Two black slip-on shoes are on the floor next to the coat rack.

Center stage is a Victorian couch, ornately patterned and draped with dark red silk. Two armchairs sit on either side of the couch. In front of the couch stands a coffee table, low to the floor and accented with a small green-hued lamp. On the coffee table: a deck of tarot cards, a bowl of seashells, an antique desk clock, and a scrapbook. Just behind the couch is a fireplace, its brick exterior stained with soot. On the mantel above the fireplace are various items, including a vase, Roman candles, and a box of long-reach matches.

Stage left stands a medium-sized oval table surrounded by four chairs. A crystal ball sits on top of the table. Behind the table in the corner looms a bookcase crowded with medical textbooks, dragon statues, decorative glass jars, and other Gothic stage dressing. To the left of the bookcase on the wall there is a painting of something not quite human, a gloomy, abstract shape that could be the silhouette of a large animal. Beneath the painting is a small desk with several drawers. A vintage marble pinball game leans against the wall on top of the desk.

Far stage left is a set of glass double-doors that leads to the woods and ocean far beyond. There is a table to the right of the doors that showcases an old-fashioned record player and a rotary telephone. A black carrying case of record albums has been placed beneath the table.

Performances of "The Satanist" will be limited to audiences of 10. Audience members will sit as close to the stage as possible. The audience is encouraged to participate in the performance and will be asked to move to and from their chairs throughout the show. All special effects depend on the production value of the performance, but many of the requirements (such as sound recordings, breakaway glass, and glowing lights) can be easily and inexpensively obtained.

At Rise: The living room at Summit Drive is near-dark. The audience can just make out a female shape reclining on the couch, and a tall, upright male figure sitting in the armchair stage left.

CAROLINE: You were late from the hospital. Darla had left by then, and I was alone, trying to fall asleep on the couch. The glass doors were wide open. I thought listening to the ocean would help me rest. It took me hours, but eventually I drifted off to sleep.

In the background, the whistling wind and the crashing of distant waves.

CAROLINE: Deep in the night, a terrible sound jarred me awake. It was an agonizing sound. The sound of something in great distress. As moonlight poured through the open doors, I realized what the sound was. It was the bleating of a goat. A goat in terrible pain. The poor thing was screaming.

In addition to the bleating of the goat, we now hear the howling of dogs, the low-pitched bellow of bullfrogs, the hissing of snakes, and the twittering of birds.

CAROLINE: It was as if the entire forest had come alive. The sound of every animal grated on my ears. I stood up from the couch and approached the glass doors, the light of the moon guiding my path. But I could see nothing outside. Only the tangled black branches of the wood, the towering monsters of the trees. And so I shut the doors and returned to the couch. I closed my eyes tight, put pillows over my ears, and longed for sleep.

The cry of the panicked, bleating goat comes again.

CAROLINE: But I heard it again—the shrill and mournful wail, like that of a prisoner on the way to his own execution! I took the pills from your medical bag and swallowed two of them dry, hoping they would force me into a night of dreamless sleep. But just as they began to take their drowsy effect, I saw something in the shaft of moonlight. Something floating in the room like vapor. The object began to take on shape and form…it was a pair of enormous hands, the knuckles raw and bloodied. One hand reached toward me as if to throttle my neck, while the other gripped something wet and thin and furry. Whatever it was, it was dripping with blood!

Dim light slowly begins to emerge from the green-hued lamp on the coffee table and the wall sconces throughout the set. CAROLINE FORSYTHE, 30s, reclines on the couch, a sad-eyed but beautiful woman dressed in a black nightgown. MANUEL FORSYTHE, 40s, sits in the armchair stage left, dressed in a cardinal-red smoking jacket, black trousers, and black slippers.

CAROLINE: Suddenly, I felt myself being turned over onto my stomach—turned against my will! My nightgown was ripped open with ease, exposing my backside. I felt a sharp prickling along my spine. I started to scream for help, but no one could hear me. I felt strong hands pinning me down. I heard laughter—a woman's cruel laughter! And a rotting smell—like dung! I began calling for you—my beloved husband. "Help me, Manuel! Help me!"

MANUEL: I'm here now, Caroline. No one can hurt you.

CAROLINE: It was the single most terrifying nightmare of my life. If you hadn't come home and woken me up, I don't know what would have happened.

MANUEL: Dreams are a fascinating outlet for the human mind, but they are not real. You must remember that.

CAROLINE: But symbolically—it must have meant something!

MANUEL: It only means that electrical stimuli pulled random thoughts and experiences from your subconscious. We all have nightmares, Caroline—they're perfectly normal.

CAROLINE: But it felt so real!

MANUEL: Was there any proof that the events you described in your dream actually took place? Was your nightgown torn? Were there drops of blood on the floor?

CAROLINE: Of course not. And there was no one else in the house when you came home. I know how silly it all sounds, and yet I can't help but feel—oh, Manuel! I want to leave Summit Drive! I want to leave here for good!

MANUEL: This is our home, Caroline. A place you once loved. We've made a life here.

CAROLINE: But we're in the middle of nowhere. Our nearest neighbor is over two miles away—the hospital even farther. And the house is too big—I get lost in all the rooms! Something evil lives here, Manuel—maybe not in the house itself, but out there in the woods! Don't tell me you haven't heard the noises. Night after night—the shrieking birds, the barking dogs, the screaming cattle!

MANUEL: There's a dog kennel just past Moore Creek, and Mr. Carmody brands his livestock to ward off rustlers and common thieves. It's nothing to be alarmed about.

Just then, the sound of tumbling ocean waves and the loud screeching of a seagull can be heard from stage left.

CAROLINE: Did you hear that? That gull is being tortured!

MANUEL: It's merely scavenging for food. Coastal seagulls can be quite active at night.

CAROLINE: (*Unable to help herself*). Well, you have an answer for everything, don't you? (*Beat*) I didn't mean that, Manuel. But I'm scared to be alone here. It's not just the strange noises. When I do see our neighbors—why, they're up to very queer things! Just the other day, while on my walk, I spotted Mr. Carmody digging a hole in the ground with his bare hands. He was out by the cemetery, up to his elbows in dirt...and what looked like blood. I think he had killed an animal...and was burying it! And Mrs. Jory walks along the shore at night without a stitch of clothing on—naked as a jaybird! I don't trust these people, Manuel. I know you enjoy their company from time to time, but please—don't make me stay another night in this house alone!

MANUEL: I have a very important surgery first thing in the morning, darling. I must go to the hospital tonight to meet with my team and discuss every detail of the procedure.

CAROLINE: Oh, Manuel, not tonight! You can leave early in the morning, after the sun's come up. You're one of the most gifted and dedicated surgeons in the world, but you need your rest!

MANUEL: Caroline, you can't ask me to abandon my duties at the hospital. A woman's life is at stake.

CAROLINE: (*Taking a deep, reassuring breath*). Oh, you're right. I know you're right! (*Beat*) It is an important surgery?

MANUEL: One for the medical history books—if we're successful.

CAROLINE: (*Resolute*). Then go. Save that woman's life and don't worry about your melodramatic wife back at home. I'll be fine.

MANUEL: Why not take the car to town and stay with Darla?

CAROLINE: (*Standing and moving toward the coat rack*). Sisters can only spend so much time with each other before they're clawing at one another's throats. Besides, I need to learn to conquer my fears on my own. I'm a big girl. (*Takes the black cloak from the rack*) It's a quarter to seven, dear. (*Struggling to be brave*). Come take your coat.

MANUEL: (*Stands and begins removing his smoking jacket. Approaches Caroline at the coat rack and exchanges his jacket for the black cloak. Removes his slippers and replaces them with the black slip-on shoes*). Now, Caroline, humor me for a moment and take a look around this house. Look at all the trinkets we've collected from our travels throughout the world. Those tarot cards from Spain. The crystal ball from that open-air market in Burma. All my rare medical journals and books. Why, we're just as eccentric as our neighbors, if not more so.

CAROLINE: Are you suggesting I regard them as kindred spirits?

MANUEL: (*Takes Caroline in his arms and kisses her*). I'm suggesting you not worry so much. We moved to Summit Drive to get away from the violence and crime of the big city. You're safe here.

CAROLINE: (*Considering something*). Manuel?

MANUEL: What is it?

CAROLINE: (*Hesitant*). I couldn't help but notice—your hands. They're scratched. And your knuckles—is that dried blood?

MANUEL: (*Studies his hands*). Oh—yes. My eczema flared up last night after you went to bed. I couldn't stop scratching. I'll soak them in vinegar when I get to the hospital. (*Moves toward door stage right and takes a key from one of the hooks on the wall*). Well, wish me luck, my darling. I'll be home sometime in the late morning. We'll have brunch together. Steak and eggs.

CAROLINE: (*Goes to the door and opens it for him*). Good night, Manuel. And good luck.

Manuel kisses Caroline on the cheek before exiting through the door stage right. Caroline turns to the audience and addresses them directly.

CAROLINE: My friends—you must help me! We have not a moment to spare. You see, time moves much faster here at Summit Drive. It's as if we're in some other dimension...a twilight zone of sorts. Here! See for yourself! (*Caroline picks up the antique desk clock and hands it to an audience member*). See how quickly the slow hand moves. See how it glows in your hand. (*The clock begins to glow a bright green*). Pass it around if you need to, but we don't have much time! (*As the audience examines the glowing clock, Caroline pulls the right-side armchair forward and sits before them*). Please—allow me to explain. A few nights ago, while my husband was at work, I discovered something in this room that turned my blood to ice. Ever since then, I've been convinced that he's going to kill me! I was looking through our bookcase, searching for something juicy to read, when I came across an old newspaper clipping. And what I read there scared me half to death! I didn't want Manuel to grow suspicious, so I returned the clipping to its hiding spot—only now, it's gone. If you can help me find it again, I can prove to you that I'm telling the truth!

With Caroline's aid, the audience begins searching the living room at Summit Drive. They will be encouraged to interact with the physical space, following Caroline's lead but also venturing off on their own. Searching for the newspaper article might involve rummaging through the desk, examining the painting and the books, looking inside the fireplace or vase or galoshes, leafing through the scrapbook, peeking under tables and chairs and couch cushions, thumbing through the tarot cards, and poking around in the record sleeves. Caroline will also have some fun with the audience, coaxing them to play with the marble pinball machine, tell "fortunes" with the crystal ball, or even play an "old timey" record on the phonograph.

Eventually, someone in the audience will discover the newspaper clipping, which the director of the production can choose to hide in any number of spots (e.g., inside the box of long matches, in a hidden compartment within the desk, or tucked into a medical journal on the bookcase). The actress playing Caroline can also "hide" the clipping while the audience is distracted, giving them more time to explore the space. Once the clipping is discovered, Caroline will guide the audience members back to their seats.

CAROLINE: (*Overjoyed*). I knew I could count on you all—thank you! (*Turns toward the audience member who found the newspaper clipping*). I don't know if I can bear to voice its horrors again. Would you mind so much to read it aloud for us?

AUDIENCE MEMBER: (*Reading article*): "From the University of Vermont College of Medicine newspaper, 1986. A group of second-year medical students who were planning a satanic 'black mass' were forced off campus on Saturday night after a public outcry from other students, staff, and administration. The intended ceremony, which would have included an animal sacrifice, even caused a priest from the Christ Memorial Church to hold a Eucharistic procession in an effort to ward off any evil spirits that the medical students may have conjured up through their activities and behavior."

CAROLINE: Now—take a look at that photograph next to the article. I know it's old and fuzzy, but look closely. Pass it down the line so that everyone can see. That's Manuel. That's my husband! My husband is a Satanist!

Suddenly, soft yellow light filters from above the stage.

CAROLINE: (*Panicked*). Morning! Already! Quick—let me have that!

Caroline takes the newspaper clipping from the audience member currently holding it and hides it beneath the armchair cushion. She fusses with her hair and straightens her gown—then turns to the audience.

CAROLINE: (*Barely a whisper*). Not a word about any of this.

The front door opens and Manuel enters. Underneath his black cloak he wears pale-green medical scrubs. The front is spotted with blood.

MANUEL: Ah, good morning, Caroline! I thought you would still be asleep.

CAROLINE: (*Trying to remain calm*). You know me. I barely got a wink.

MANUEL: (*Hanging up cloak on the rack*). Another nightmare?

CAROLINE: No, I…I didn't allow myself to sleep long enough for one to settle in.

MANUEL: Then what did you do all night? (*Looks around suspiciously*). This living room looks…disturbed.

CAROLINE: I…kept myself occupied. Read a little bit. Listened to some records. I even saw my future in our little crystal ball there.

MANUEL: Oh? And what did you see?

CAROLINE: (*Despondent*). I saw a dark wood. Cold and damp. A pair of muddy boots. And a pile of dirt that looked like a burial mound.

MANUEL: (*Goes to her, tenderly*). I thought we would have a meal together, but you need to sleep. I want you to take two—no, *three*—of those pills I brought home from the hospital.

CAROLINE: (*Parts from him and begins tidying up the room*). That reminds me—how did the operation go?

MANUEL: Erm…it was postponed. My surgical team and I decided we weren't quite ready.

CAROLINE: But you said the woman's life was at stake. And your scrubs—they're spotted with blood.

MANUEL: She's stabilized. By tomorrow we should have everything in place. As for the blood—a boy was brought into the ER. He had been struck by a car. We did all we could…but he died early this morning.

CAROLINE: (*As if in another world*). The stench of death—it hangs over everything.

MANUEL: (*Sits on the couch*). Really, Caroline—what has gotten into you?

CAROLINE: (*With sudden anger*). I should ask you the same thing!

MANUEL: Now you're just trying to pick a fight.

CAROLINE: (*With great courage*). I know the truth, Manuel. I know what you are—what you have always been!

MANUEL: Oh, really?

CAROLINE: I found out! The newspaper clipping you tried so cleverly to hide. You're a Satanist! A devil worshipper!

MANUEL: That clipping? (*Laughs—deep and hearty*). Oh, Caroline, I can't believe you fell for that!

CAROLINE: Why the hell are you laughing?

MANUEL: Did you happen to check the date on that newspaper article? I doubt that you did—you were too caught up trying to prove that your devoted husband once entered into a pact with Lucifer. But if you had checked the date, you would have noticed that the article was published on April 1st, 1986. (*Beat as he lets this information sink in*). It was April Fool's Day, Caroline. The article was published as a joke!

CAROLINE: A joke?

MANUEL: Yes—it's a college tradition! In that very same issue, we printed an interview with a talking horse and an editorial about Ronald Reagan's boxer shorts! From what I can recall, there was even an op-ed piece that demanded the school cafeteria start serving lobster burgers and beer on tap. (*As Caroline cowers away*). Caroline, honey—you're overreacting.

CAROLINE: I don't believe you. You're lying!

MANUEL: (*Rises and goes to her, angry now*). Listen to me, woman! This madness has got to stop!

CAROLINE: (*Sidesteps his advances*). No—keep away from me! Don't touch me ever again!

MANUEL: You're out of control. Your pills—you need your pills. Let me get them.

CAROLINE: I'm never taking those pills again. You're always trying to bully me into taking them. To keep me sedated. All so you can run naked in the woods with our neighbors, killing animals and God knows what else! (*She darts to the open doorway that leads to the upstairs*).

MANUEL: Caroline! Just where do you think you're going?

CAROLINE: I'm going out! You're not the only one who gets to leave this house on a whim!

MANUEL: (*Wheedling*). But you'll be all alone. There will be no one to look out for you.

CAROLINE: That's what you think! Don't worry—I'll be back. And when I return, we will settle this once and for all!

Caroline bounds up the stairs, disappearing offstage.

MANUEL: (*Gravely*). Oh, Caroline. You're making a terrible mistake.

As the onstage lights dim, the portrait on the wall begins to glow. As the silhouette glows, it takes on the shape and image of a half-man, half-goat with horns and a wide, grinning mouth.

The curtain falls.

ACT II

Setting: *A wilderness of skeletal trees, fog, and stars. Silhouettes of birds and other creatures loom in the treetops. The stage is almost entirely dark, but a snaking row of crumbling headstones has formed a crude path from stage left to stage right. Surrounding the graves are dry leaves, broken twigs, and other stage dressing to replicate a forest (e.g., small plants, moss, boulders, stones).*

Far stage left, in the darkness, a mound of earth pierced with a large shovel. High above, a blood-red moon casts an unearthly shine.

Prior to curtain, the audience is provided two small flashlights, which they can pass around and use to illuminate different parts of the forest and cemetery. Directing their beams, they can read the inscriptions on the headstones, spot a "snake" slithering through the brush, and discover ghostly faces in the tree trunks.

At rise: The forest and cemetery are empty, though the humming of insects and the chirping of birds can be heard in the distance. A wind howls through the trees. Caroline Forsythe creeps in stage left. She is dressed in a coat and scarf. Moving stealthily, she approaches the audience.

CAROLINE: (*Whispering*). My friends—thank heavens you're still here. I'm sorry to drag you into this madness, but we must act fast. I drove to town today, going in and out of shops, sitting in the library, my mind reeling over what to do. And then it came to me! Time and time again, I've had dreams of this place. Surely this location must be important. Quickly, now—I need two of you to take those flashlights and search the cemetery with me. Come!

Urged on by Caroline, two audience volunteers will come forward with their flashlights. Caroline will guide them stage left to the start of the path, standing in front of them so that she can control the pace and direction of their search.

CAROLINE: (*To the volunteers*). Tread carefully and use your flashlights to guide you. If you spot something suspicious, bring it to our attention!

As the trio follows the crooked cemetery path, they will discover these items in the following order: a pair of bloody gardening gloves, a woman's white blouse, and a little black book of ancient rituals and spells.

When the bloody gardening gloves are found:

CAROLINE: I recognize those gloves! They belong to Mr. Carmody, the old rancher who lives up the mountain. Shine your light on them —now what does that look like to you? (*In response*). That's right—blood! I caught him digging a hole around these parts—and the more I think about it, he had a sack with him! And something was moving in the sack—something alive!

When the white blouse is found:

CAROLINE: (*Examining the blouse*). Cheap material. Size large, taken out in the bust. Several of the buttons popped off. I detect an unusual scent. (*Smells*). Clove powder—used for witchcraft! And look here—see the stitching? That's handmade. This blouse belongs to Mrs. Jory! By day she masquerades as a seamstress, but I'm convinced she's the devil's servant. She probably cast this blouse aside while surrendering her bosom to Satan himself!

And lastly, when the book of rituals and spells is found:

CAROLINE: (*Taking the book and instructing the two volunteers*). Let me see that—here, shine your light on its cover. Yes—just as I suspected! I've seen books like this in my husband's study. We've traveled the world—"only for pleasure," Manuel says—but I know better! It's so he can track down ancient, forbidden texts like this one. Look there— a page that's been dog-eared. (*Gives the book to one of the volunteers*). You— hold your light over the page. And you—please read what you see— I'm too scared to look!

AUDIENCE VOLUNTEER: (*Reading*): "Hail, Ancient Serpent! Ruler of the infernal underground! Dragon of hell, who wakens our spirits and cleanses our souls! Hail, Ancient Serpent, and accept this gift, our blood sacrifice, the Sabbatic Goat! To the Prince of Darkness we offer its solemn body. Its horns and tail may we put to our use in symbolic operation, a ritual experiment we conduct in Satan's name."

CAROLINE: (*Reacting*). Symbolic operation? Ritual experiment? My God, what do they have planned? (*To the two volunteers*). Quickly, leave the items where you found them and return to your seats. We can't let anyone know we've been here. (*Suddenly, the crunching of heavy boots through the brush*). Flashlights off! Silence! (*Caroline edges along stage left, moving along the path of tombstones as the footsteps grow louder. She whispers her next line*). Who's there?

From far stage left the SEXTON shambles out, an ornery but likable old man dressed in filthy dungarees and a floppy hat. His face smudged with grime, he carries a large, glowing lantern that lights his path.

SEXTON: I should be asking you the same thing, ma'am. What the hell're you doing out here at this time of night?

CAROLINE: Oh, I'm so sorry to disturb you. I didn't know this cemetery had a caretaker.

SEXTON: Well, it don't. Not officially, anyway. I'm in charge of Pioneer Hill, which is much closer to town. But city officials got wind of some hijinks going on 'round here, and they sent me to check it out. Grave-robbin', illegal diggin'—that's my business. What's yours?

CAROLINE: Well, I—I'm not sure. I came out here because...well, because I need to prove something to myself. I need to prove...that I'm not crazy. Can you understand that?

SEXTON: Not at all. Who're you, anyway?

CAROLINE: My name is Caroline Forsythe. I live at Summit Drive.

SEXTON: Ay, the doctor's wife.

CAROLINE: (*Dismally*). Is that all I am? Yes, I suppose that's true. I've been "the doctor's wife" for many years now.

SEXTON: (*Removes his hat out of respect*). Oh, I didn't mean it like that, ma'am. Why, I've seen your name in the papers, donatin' to charities and givin' alms. You strike me as a good woman. A woman with character and dignity.

CAROLINE: That's nice of you to say. I was born into a great deal of money, but I never had much use for it myself. I always thought there were people more deserving and needful than I. (*Lost in thought now*). I met my husband in Mexico. I was there to build houses for the poor, and Manuel was conducting business with a local pharmacy. I fell in love with him…or did I? I'm not sure anymore. What a dupe I was—do you know it was my money that allowed us to purchase the house on Summit Drive? I was blinded by Manuel's good looks, his love of adventure, and his desire to change the world through medicine. And now I fear that my blindness may have prevented me from seeing the evil that lurks within his heart.

SEXTON: (*Beat*). Y'know, it's quite a coincidence I bumped into you, especially here, at the witchin' hour.

CAROLINE: What makes you say that?

SEXTON: I was here last night, lookin' for signs of suspicious activity. Tryin' to catch the perpetrators in the act, y'see. Only I didn't bring a strong enough light, the fool I am. But I thought I seen your husband creepin' about. Does he have muttonchops? And wear a long black cloak and big ol' galoshes?

CAROLINE: (*Frightened*). Why—yes, that's him!

SEXTON: He was with some other folk—another man and a lady as big as a double-wide. This is gonna sound a little strange, but I think I caught 'em dancing.

CAROLINE: Dancing?

SEXTON: They were hoopin' and hollerin', acting funny and chanting some kind of religious song. Like an old spiritual, but real witchy. When I shone my light on 'em, they took off in fright. I hope you don't mind me saying, but the lady they was with—she was tip-to-tail naked!

CAROLINE: Can you show me where you saw them?

SEXTON: Mrs. Forsythe, ma'am, I know you have your own reasons for sneakin' through a boneyard in the dead of night, and I'm to believe it has something to do with that husband of yours. But based on what I seen last night, I think you should leave here this instant. This ain't no place for a lady of your quality.

CAROLINE: Please—just point me in the right direction. I have a flashlight.

SEXTON: There's evil goings-on in these woods—I fear it. You best stay away. Follow me to my truck and let me take you home.

CAROLINE: You don't understand—my life is at stake! (*Almost to herself*). My life is at stake...wait a minute. It's me...I'm the woman on the operating table. I'm the one undergoing surgery! "One for the medical history books," Manuel said! What did that little black book call it...a ritual experiment! (*To the sexton*). Please, sir—no fooling now. Take me to the very spot you saw my husband and his friends.

SEXTON: (*Gives in, somewhat afraid*). Well, you are a persistent one. It's actually right this way. Follow me. (*They walk stage left to the mound of earth with the shovel in it*). It was right here. (*Holds up lantern*). Looks like they was doin' some diggin'. Careful where you step, ma'am. There's a hole here that looks to be about four feet deep.

CAROLINE: (*Peering in*). Is there...is there something inside it?

SEXTON: (*Crouches on one knee*). I can't see too good...it's as dark as a dungeon out here. You hold the lantern and let me feel 'round inside. (*Passes the lantern to Caroline, then reaches as deep as he can into the hole*). Ay, something wet! Smells like copper! (*He holds up his hand in the light—it's slick with blood. Caroline gasps with fear*). Christ on a bike! What the hell were they up to last night? Hold that light steady, ma'am—I think I see somethin'. (*Crouches on all fours and leans into the hole. He gets a good look, then sits back up, on his haunches, stunned and hard of breath*).

CAROLINE: (*Afraid to ask*). What...what did you see?

SEXTON: (*With genuine sadness*). A dead goat. Torn limb from limb, the poor thing. They even cut off its horns and tail.

CAROLINE: My God!

SEXTON: (*Stands up*). Take my arm, Mrs. Forsythe. We need to get you out of here. This is the devil's work, you can bet.

As Caroline reaches for the Sexton's hand, a masked and cloaked FIGURE rises from behind the headstones stage right. The Figure knocks Caroline to the floor, causing the lantern to shatter. The stage dims as the Figure grabs the Sexton and drags him, kicking and hollering, center.

CAROLINE: Let that man go! He didn't do anything to you!

THE FIGURE: (*To the Sexton*): Your children are next, worthless scum! You've made your living among the dead—now join them!

. The Figure withdraws a knife from his cloak, raises it, and begins stabbing the Sexton, grunting with every blow. Gouts of "blood" shower the stage and the audience.

THE FIGURE: (*Dragging the body*): Into the hole with you, old man! Into the grave! (*The Figure hurls the Sexton's body into the hole, then turns on Caroline.*) Ungrateful sow! You rich bitch! The time for your transformation has come!

CAROLINE: (*Standing, running stage right and off*): No! Keep away from me! Keep away!

The curtain falls as the Figure lunges after Catherine stage right.

ACT III

Setting: *Back inside the living room at Summit Drive.*

At rise: *The living room is dark, the shadows rippling from the lit candles on the mantel above the fireplace. The muddy galoshes are gone from the doorway and Manuel's cloak no longer hangs on the rack. Torn and dirtied, Caroline's coat and scarf hang there instead.*

In the darkness the audience can make out Caroline resting on the couch, her body wrapped in a shawl. In the armchair stage right sits another woman, who leans in close to Caroline.

CAROLINE: (*With fatigue*). I ran as fast as I could through the woods, passing by all sorts of nightmarish sights. A dog with its belly ripped open. The skull of a cow nailed to a tree. And birds—so many birds—gutted, lining the forest floor in gruesome patterns, their eyes swollen shut in death. Somehow I made it back to the house, my clothes torn by branches that seemed to lunge for me like animal claws. I thought of that black figure in the woods—the sound of his voice, the very *stink* of him—and my entire body shuddered with dread and fear. How he killed that poor man who was only trying to help me! I wanted to fall asleep and pretend it was all a horrific dream.

DARLA: (*Comforting*). Try not to upset yourself, Caroline. You're going to be all right. You're in your own home, safe as can be.

The green-hued lamp on the coffee table and the wall sconces throughout the set begin to shine, bathing the stage in an almost ethereal glow. DARLA MONTGOMERY, 40s, sits near Caroline, occasionally reaching out a reassuring hand. Darla is dressed stylishly in a sweater dress and over-the-knee boots.

CAROLINE: (*Sweetly*). I opened my eyes and there you were—my big sister. You've always been there, ever since Mother and Father died. To comfort me. To take care of me. (*With a sob in her voice*). To rescue me.

DARLA: Hush with that kind of talk. Now, you must be hungry—you've been sleeping for over 19 hours. Why don't I make you something to eat? Or maybe you'd like some tea with honey?

CAROLINE: (*Sits up, alarmed*). 19 hours? Wait a minute…where's Manuel?

DARLA: Night shift at the hospital. He went out searching for you when you disappeared. After several hours he gave up, only to return here to find you passed out on this couch. He was terribly worried, but he didn't want to disturb your slumber. Before he left for work, he called and asked me to come over and keep an eye on you. He was practically crying, he was so upset.

CAROLINE: Crocodile tears, every one of them!

DARLA: (*Stunned*). First you go running out into the woods in the dead of night like a crazy person. Then you tell me you witnessed a murder. Now you're turning your back on your husband, who's done nothing but love and honor you! Caroline, what's the matter? What's really going on here?

CAROLINE: You've always been the more sensible one, so I don't know how much of this you're going to believe. I used to think I was losing my mind, but now…now I know better.

DARLA: Please—tell me. You have me scared half to death.

CAROLINE: Manuel is a Satanist. I don't know for how long, but at least since he was in college. He belongs to a cult that he and our neighbors put together. They conduct strange rituals in the woods, where they dance naked and sacrifice animals.

DARLA: (*Stands, shocked*). Caroline! What on earth are you talking about?

CAROLINE: (*Stands, remaining firm*). There's more, Darla. I went to the place in the forest where they hold their gatherings. I found a dead goat with its horns and tail removed and a black book—the devil's book—that described some kind of operation.

DARLA: An operation? I don't understand.

CAROLINE: (*Goes to the portrait of the goat on the wall*). Did you know that when I married Manuel, *this* was his most prized possession? Not a family heirloom or an antique piece of furniture, but *this* picture— this disgusting creature!

DARLA: So your husband has terrible taste in art. That's not a crime, Caroline.

CAROLINE: That's where you're wrong! This portrait represents the blackest evil! Come here and look carefully. (*Darla hesitates*). Darla, he could be home any minute. Come over here and look! (*Darla goes, reluctantly*). Now what do you see?

DARLA: It looks like a faun. One of those half-man, half-goat creatures from Roman mythology.

CAROLINE: Ha! That's what Manuel always told me—but the devil is a liar! (*Pacing the living room now*). That's a portrait of Baphomet, the Sabattic goat, the official symbol of the Church of Satan! I think Manuel and his friends have something terrible in store for me!

DARLA: Oh, Caroline—

CAROLINE: I've had nightmares. Manuel's blood-stained hands reaching for me. He's holding something wet and dripping…why, I see it now. It looks like...it looks like a tail! He rips my nightgown open from the back. He wants to put that tail on me! And the horns—that's why they removed them from the goat! They want to turn me into a monster!

DARLA: Caroline, I've never heard such blasphemous thoughts!

CAROLINE: Just tell me you'll help me, Darla—please!

DARLA: (*Backing up toward the front door, scared now*). Of course I will help you. I always have. But perhaps I should—

CAROLINE: Where are you going?

DARLA: (*Her back to the door now, her hand reaching behind her for the doorknob*). To the market. You need something to eat. Something fresh and hearty. A bowl of tomato soup, or a nice beef stew—

CAROLINE: The nearest market is miles from here! Don't lie to me, Darla! Don't leave me here to face that man on my own!

As Darla whirls around to flee the house, Caroline darts to the revolver hanging on the wall. She uses her elbow to smash the glass, then snatches the gun from the case. Caroline keeps the gun at her side, not pointing it directly at Darla—but not putting it away. A moment of tension passes between the two sisters.

DARLA: Have you lost your mind?

CAROLINE: (*Desperate*). I'm not going to shoot you. You're my sister and I love you with all my heart. But I don't know what else to do to make you stay.

DARLA: You can start by thinking rationally. You can start by putting that gun away.

CAROLINE: Step away from that door and I will.

Just then, a bleating goat cries out from somewhere in the woods, startling Caroline.

CAROLINE: There it is again—a sure promise of demonic forces at work! (*Darla uses the distraction to fling open the door and run out of the house, offstage*). Darla, no! Come back! (*Accepting that Darla has fled, Caroline lowers the gun and turns toward the audience*). It's just us now, I suppose. Oh, please, don't be afraid. I don't want to hurt anyone. Here—take this. It's probably better that way. (*Hands the gun to one of the audience members*). I can't escape these images in my mind! That poor caretaker, slaughtered before my very eyes. And I can't help but think Manuel must have been the killer. Did you notice? (*Walks to the front door*). His galoshes are gone. He probably needed them to make his way through the swampy woods! And over here—this bookcase! (*Hurries to the bookcase and scans the shelves*). Just listen to some of these titles: *Genetic Mutants and Human Curiosities, Medical Experiments of the Third Reich, A Victorian Surgeon's Scrapbook*. Oh, the clues were everywhere! And now, as I see it, I have only two choices. Allow myself to become a victim to my husband's perverse ideas, or call the police and risk being hauled away to the mental ward. (*Considering*). Well, I don't like my odds, but it's a chance I'll have to take. (*Picks up the rotary phone and dials the police station. After a pause, SERGEANT McGEE'S voice can be heard, crackling through the sound system*).

McGEE: Pioneer Hill Police Department. This is Sergeant McGee.

CAROLINE: Hello—yes—police? I need your help.

McGEE: What can I do for you, ma'am?

CAROLINE: My name is Caroline Forsythe, and I live at 1919 Summit Drive. I need you to send an officer to my house right away. This is going to sound crazy but—I think my husband is planning to kill me tonight.

McGEE: Come again?

CAROLINE: Listen, he's murdered someone already! There's a body, in the ground, in the old cemetery past Moore Creek. Go see for yourself if you want proof, but I need an officer here immediately! Manuel will be home any minute!

McGEE: Take it easy, take it easy. Let's start with some basics. What's your name?

CAROLINE: Caroline Forsythe! I told you already!

McGEE: Oh, wait. Aren't you the doctor's wife? Yes, I remember now. He warned me you might be calling.

CAROLINE: (*Horrified*). What? *Why?*

McGEE: He said you were suffering from some kind of psychological illness. Nightmares, delusional thinking, real heavy-duty stuff. He's a good guy, your husband. He donates to the Fallen Officer Foundation every year.

CAROLINE: Unbelievable! You're siding with him, too! Just like Darla!

McGEE: Please calm down, Mrs. Forsythe. There's no need to raise your voice. (*Beat*). Tell you what. Why don't you give me your address, and I'll have a patrol car out there in an hour. How does that sound?

CAROLINE: Oh, forget it! (*Slams down the phone. As the reality of her situation hits her, she bursts into tears. After a brief crying jag, Caroline hears the sound of a car roaring up into the front drive*). That's his car! He's coming! The lights—I must turn them all out! (*Rushes about the stage, turning off the wall sconces and the green-hued lamp. The stage turns dark. Caroline faces the audience*). My friends—thank God you're still here. One of you—help me barricade the door! (*With the assistance of an audience volunteer, Caroline blocks the front door with the couch, dragging it length-wise across the entry way*). This should buy us some time—maybe convince him into going away! Please keep very still and don't say a word. (*The volunteer returns to his or her seat as Caroline crouches by one of the center chairs. She uses this moment to slyly take back the gun from the audience member who was holding it. A few tense seconds pass, and then the sound of footsteps outside, the rattling of a key in the lock. Then a sudden, powerful force trying to barge its way into the house, the door smashing into the couch*).

MANUEL: (*Off*). Caroline, what is the meaning of this? Let me in! This is *my* house! (*More banging, the sound of splintering wood. When this proves ineffective, Manuel speaks gently*). Oh, Caroline, I have your pills! Come swallow your pills, my darling! (*And then with maniacal rage*). Come swallow your pills, you disgusting pig!

CAROLINE: Just go away, Manuel! I don't love you anymore! I don't think I've ever loved you! (*Caroline's words are met with silence. She stands slowly, picks up the green-hued lamp, and clicks it on. Then she creeps her way center stage, using the lamp to guide her way*). I think—I think he's gone. (*She edges toward the door, trying to peer through the peephole*). It's so dark outside—I can't see a thing. (*As Caroline kneels on the couch and attempts to look through the peephole, the glass doors stage right creak open. Unbeknownst to Caroline, Manuel steps through the doors and into the living room. He wears his mud-stained galoshes and carries a bloodied burlap sack over his shoulder. His right arm hangs limply at his side).*

MANUEL: *(With grim affect).* I hurt my hand, Caroline. *(Caroline whirls around, screams).* That's your fault. If only you hadn't barricaded the door. If only you had let me in, like an obedient wife should.

CAROLINE: Those doors were locked! *(Looks at the key hook on the wall—all the keys are missing).* What have you done?

MANUEL: *(Approaches slowly).* I took every key for this house and made a nice little necklace for myself. *(Reaches into his shirt and reveals a chain necklace made up of house keys).* I knew I might have to sneak my way in someday. Or perhaps—lock *you* in, for all of eternity.

CAROLINE: *(Cowering, terrified).* How long—how long have you been planning on hurting me?

MANUEL: *(With evil relish).* Since the day we first met, you ignorant cow. *(Caroline points the gun at Manuel).* What are you doing with my gun? That's a precious antique.

CAROLINE: An antique that can still shoot you in the gut. Don't you remember? You once showed me how to fire it.

MANUEL: *(Continues to approach, slowly).* Caroline, I'm warning you...

CAROLINE: I will give you one chance. One chance to save your precious skin. Leave now and promise never to come back.

MANUEL: Not on your life. Give me that gun.

CAROLINE: No!

MANUEL: Mr. Carmody and Mrs. Jory are waiting outside, Caroline. They're waiting for *you.* Would you like me to call them in? Carmody brought his branding iron and his carving knives, and Jory— well, I think she wants to take a bite right out of your pretty little rump!

CAROLINE: You don't scare me, Manuel, and neither do they! Take one more step and I'll fire.

MANUEL: *(Drops the sack from his shoulder and steps forward).* Now you listen to me— *(Caroline fires two shots, but Manuel remains standing, unaffected).* You stupid, stupid girl.

CAROLINE: (*Disbelieving*). But I shot you! I shot you! (*Caroline fires four more times, causing Manuel to burst in deranged laughter*). The gun is empty! But how—?

MANUEL: When you enter into a blood pact with Satan, you are granted certain protections from the mortal world—spiritual armor, if you will. Your bullets can't hurt me now.

CAROLINE: (*Drops the gun, surrendering*). What are you going to do to me?

MANUEL: I'm going to turn you into the devil's concubine. (*Reaches into the sack and withdraws a furry tail*). Half-woman, half-goat. (*Withdraws a pair of severed goat horns*). A creature to be idolized—a gift for Satan! A transplant surgery demanded by the Son of Perdition himself!

CAROLINE: You're insane! Totally insane!

MANUEL: (*Places the tail and horns on the coffee table, then pulls a knife from his coat pocket*). Recognize this knife? It's the same one I killed that old caretaker with. The same one that I will use to cut into your forehead and spine. And if you offer any resistance, the same knife I will use to slit your throat.

CAROLINE: Manuel! Please!

MANUEL: Oh, don't worry. Carmody, Jory, and I—we've practiced the procedure many times before. All those poor people and animals! The howling dogs and screaming gulls. All those pitiful goats. They were just tools, really. Empty vessels. But their deaths were not in vain, Caroline. They died so that I could perfect my art.

CAROLINE: (*Crying*). Just kill me, please. Kill me instead.

MANUEL: (*Laughing*). Now, Caroline. Where would be the fun in that? (*Brandishes the knife*). During your little disappearing act, I took the time to prepare an operating table in the upstairs bedroom. If you play nice, I'll inject you with a healthy dose of morphine to ease the pain. But if you continue to be a brat, you won't get so much as an aspirin. (*Lunges for her with the knife*).

CAROLINE: Oh, somebody, please help me!

Caroline screams as the sudden sound of gunshots rings out and the curtain falls on the scene.

ACT IV

Setting: *Morning in the Summit Drive living room. The couch has been returned to its proper place and the front door has been closed.*

Well-lit, the living room has been restored to order as much as possible. The severed tail and horns have been removed. On the floor near the front door is a body covered with a white sheet, the sheet soaked through with blood. OFFICER BICKNELL, 30s, stands guard over the body. The glass doors stage right have been closed.

At rise: *Sergeant McGee, 50s, sits in the armchair stage right, a well-intentioned police officer with a bit of "mountain man" in him. He has a scruffy beard and wears a western-style shirt with pearl buttons. He carries a notepad and a pencil chewed to the nub. Caroline sits on the couch next to the chair, a cup of tea in her trembling hands. She has changed clothes and pulled her hair into a tangled bun.*

McGEE: I understand this is hard, Mrs. Forsythe. The medical examiner should be here soon. Please—try to continue.

CAROLINE: Manuel pulled out a knife. He wanted to perform some kind of surgery on me—to turn me into a goat! A gift for Satan! I know it sounds absurd, Sergeant McGee. Horrific and absurd.

McGEE: Your husband was a deeply disturbed man, Mrs. Forsythe.

CAROLINE: What about...the others? Mr. Carmody and Mrs. Jory?

McGEE: We've arrested them on suspicion of murder. My men found a number of dead bodies on both of their properties. (*Beat*). Your husband and his friends were sick people, Mrs. Forsythe. You would surely be dead right now were it not for your sister.

CAROLINE: Oh, Darla...I can't quite remember what happened.

McGEE: When she left your property, she immediately drove to the police station. She returned to the house with Officer Bicknell here—who happens to be an expert marksman. He took your husband out with two shots to the chest.

CAROLINE: But *I* shot Manuel first! He said it was Satan's armor that protected him from the bullets!

McGEE: Mrs. Forsythe, your husband and his friends may be murderers—they may have even started a cult—but they're not Satanists. The crystal ball, the rituals in the woods, the newspaper article, the goat tail and the horns—even the diagrams of the transplant surgery we found upstairs. These were all elaborate props your husband put together in order to deceive you.

CAROLINE: Why would he do such a thing?

McGEE: My men are still piecing together the evidence, but Manuel Forsythe hasn't worked at Pioneer Hill Hospital in quite some time. He was fired over a year ago due to negligence and misconduct.

CAROLINE: I don't understand.

McGEE: He wanted everyone to think you had lost your mind, Mrs. Forsythe. He was going to kill you, then claim he acted in self-defense. "Oh, officer, I was only protecting myself from that wild, crazy woman!" He was broke and planned to inherit all of your money after your death.

CAROLINE: But the gun!

McGEE: He knew you'd probably try to use it against him. That old gun was filled with blanks. (*Beat*). Your husband didn't have any special Satanic power, Mrs. Forsythe. He was just another cold-blooded killer and thief, like thousands of desperate men before him.

CAROLINE: (*Rubbing her temples*). I think I'm in shock. I can't believe Manuel is dead.

McGEE: Well, to be frank, I need you to identify the body for the official report. I've found that this process can actually be beneficial in accepting a tragic or violent death. The body is right over here by the door. Can you follow me? (*McGee and Caroline stand and walk over to the body near the front door. McGee motions to Officer Bicknell*). Officer Bicknell, can you lift the sheet, please?

BICKNELL: Yes, sir. (*Bicknell lifts the sheet, revealing Manuel's face to Caroline. She puts up a brave front, but eventually cries out in terror*). What is it, ma'am?

CAROLINE: His face—it's not like I imagined at all. There's a blush to his cheeks. And...and a smile on his lips! He looks...he looks alive!

McGEE: (*Motions for Bicknell to cover the body again, which he does*). He hasn't been dead very long, Mrs. Forsythe, but trust me—he's deceased. As soon as the medical examiner arrives, he will confirm the death and take the body to the morgue in Pioneer Hill. Of course, I'll need you to come down to the station and fill out a written statement of tonight's events. Then we'll put you in touch with the funeral home.

CAROLINE: Thank you, Sergeant McGee. You've been very kind. (*Beat*). Gentlemen, I know this is going to sound strange, considering all that my husband put me through. But there was a time once—a long time ago—when I think he might have been a good man. Would you mind very much if I said a private goodbye to him?

McGEE: Not a problem, Mrs. Forsythe. We understand. Officer Bicknell and I will just step outside and give you some privacy. (*The two officers exit the front door stage right. Caroline waits until the door closes before she approaches the audience. Just as she begins to speak, the stage lights dim to near darkness. The antique desk clock on the coffee table begins to glow a bright green*).

CAROLINE: Oh, the darkness—brought on by that supernatural march of time! I knew it, my friends! An ancient power stills thrives here—a power that no one will ever be able to fully explain. I'm going to leave with the officers now, far away from Summit Drive and never to return. I'll send movers for my private things. You'll leave too, I suppose—but before you— (*Just then, a "locking" sound startles Caroline*). That sound—it's the front door! (*She rushes to it, tugging on the knob*). It's locked! (*Two more "locking" sounds are heard*). The glass doors! (*Runs to the glass doors and tries them with no luck*). Locked too! His ghost—Manuel's ghost has trapped us inside! (*A raging wind begins to pass through the room and animals make strange noises from somewhere far away*). No! No! We mustn't let him take over! (*Caroline runs back to the front door, pounding on it with her fist)*. Officers! Officers, please help! I've been locked inside! Please help me! *(There's no reply. The dim stage lights flicker on and off as the wind and animals grow louder. Objects begin falling from the bookcase. A glass jar shatters. The portrait of the goat drops to the floor. Frantic, Caroline turns to the audience)*. I think the house is caving in! The keys—around his neck! It's our only chance of escape! *(Looks to Manuel's body, covered by the sheet)*. The body—the body is dead, I know that—but he'll kill me if I get too close. I know he will! A brave volunteer, please—get the keys to one of these doors. They're on a chain around a dead man's neck! *(If necessary, Caroline can lead the volunteer to the body)*. Everyone else, please, take hold of one another's hands and gather around! Our strength will keep the devil in his rightful place! *(Caroline will guide the rest of the audience to circle around the body. The volunteer will pull back the sheet to reveal Manuel's corpse. The actor playing Manuel should remain perfectly still. The chain of keys hangs from his neck, each one attached with a thin clasp. If necessary, Caroline can give some direction to the volunteer)*. Try to undo one of those clasps, if you can. Any one of those keys will do. *(As soon as the volunteer manages to grab hold of one of the keys, Manuel springs to life with a scream of his entire soul. He sits up, lunging for the audience as they scatter. Caroline shouts to the volunteer)*. Throw me the key—quickly! *(Key in hand, Caroline calls out to the audience)*. It's for the glass doors—this way, my friends! Follow me! *(The audience follows Caroline to the glass doors stage right as Manuel resurrects. He shambles toward stage right, groaning, his chest covered in blood)*.

MANUEL: *(A haunting moan)*. I'll tear your souls out! I'll turn you into my animal slaves! *(Caroline fumbles with the key as Manuel draws closer. More objects fall from the bookshelves. The records drop like dominoes. A candle tips off the mantel)*. What do you think you'll find out there? A safe haven of God's green earth? Mother Nature, all pristine and pure? If I have the power to rise from the dead, just imagine what horrors await you if you step out that door!

CAROLINE: *(Inserts key into lock)*. Got it!

MANUEL: *(So close he could reach out and grab an audience member with his hand)*. Satan compels you! He has great plans for all of you! *Do not leave my house! (Caroline hurls the doors open, ushering the audience into the safety of the wings. The doors close on Manuel's screams).*

THE END

"Changing the Face of Horror with Bobby Pruitt" by Christopher Coffey (originally published in *Haunter's Realm*, Fall, 2015, p. 4-8):

"Death Rituals" is the new extreme haunted house from Bobby Pruitt, a writer and set designer determined to put gore-fans through the most harrowing wringer in haunt history. Uniting the tropes of horror films with physical violence and aberrant role-playing, Pruitt creates haunted attractions that are gruesome, transgressive, and shamelessly chaotic. He openly admits that he feels little sympathy for the people who experience his haunts, viewing his patrons as characters in a horror simulation that he controls. With reputable production value—including convincing special effects and powerhouse acting—"Death Rituals" may be the most depraved haunted house the industry has ever seen. And the origins of the haunt are just as intriguing. In addition to horror movies, Pruitt credits his long-time girlfriend, an experimental photographer and exotic dancer known only as April Showers, as a major contributor to his creative process.

I first meet Pruitt outside of the enormous Los Angeles warehouse that will showcase "Death Rituals" when it opens this October. The 37-year-old haunt entrepreneur, who worked as lead set designer on the controversial "The World of Horrors," does not pose for photographs and carefully monitors his public image, so it was a bit surprising to lock eyes with a rakishly handsome man, whip-thin, with unruly hair to his shoulders and a jagged pink scar along his throat. Dressed in a cracked leather jacket and paint-splashed jeans, mirrored sunglasses hiding his eyes, Pruitt looks every inch the manipulative trickster. He greets me with a puckish smile as we begin our tour of the property and discuss his most masochistic haunt.

Our first stop is just around the corner of the building, where Pruitt has wheat-pasted a series of posters for "Death Rituals." Featuring stills from horror movies like *Carrie* and *The Texas Chain Saw Massacre*, the promotional content for the haunted attraction is representative of Pruitt's artistic influences and his belief that only through horrific imagery can artists discover true beauty. "But how is beauty possible when someone is being abused, screaming in pain, or dying?" Pruitt asks with a mad-scientist twinkle in his eye. "Come to my house and find out."

Though Pruitt includes a few details of his past in the press release for "Death Rituals," he refuses to divulge too much about his upbringing in a small Ohio town. He admits that he has battled depression for most of his life. He has never met his father. A few probing questions later, he reveals that he now lives with April in Los Angeles and that she will be featured as one of the performers in his new haunted attraction. "She's an alien, a dancer, a magician, and an astronaut. She's the chorus of a murder ballad. She's the tattoo on the back of my hand with the face of an animal," Pruitt says playfully. "She's my angel of abomination."

Always one to wear his influences on his sleeve, Pruitt has composed a script for "Death Rituals" that features signature lines from the splatter movies he grew up watching as a kid. "Guests will feel like they're on the set of an NC-17 horror film, but one where the director never yells cut and the camera never stops rolling," he says.

Pruitt's youthful imagination was filled with all sorts of ghoulish creatures, paving the way for a lifelong interest in the haunt industry. As a teen he visited as many haunted attractions as he could, all while developing his skills as a writer and visual artist. In his 20s he helped build sets, design costumes, and apply SFX makeup for scare-houses like "Ohio's Skeleton Maze" and "The Butcher of Kingsbury Run."

But it was his work on "The World of Horrors" in 2014 that alerted Pruitt to a new and sinister world that could be created through a haunted house attraction. He worked tirelessly on the event, with specific attention paid to "Blood Orgy," a haunt that was intended to resemble an interactive snuff film. When "Blood Orgy" fell apart due to protests and financial struggles, Pruitt decided to branch out on his own. "There's an audience out there that really wants to let their inhibitions go, to *belong* to a special group, and there are actors more than willing to cross certain boundaries to terrify someone," he says.

"Most people run away from their fear and pain. But once you accept that the world is a violent cesspool, you finally become free."

In addition to his experimental artwork and philosophical leanings, Pruitt has drawn from some of the most iconic characters in all of horror cinema for "Death Rituals," hoping that haunt enthusiasts will feel sucked right into the bloody celluloid of films like *The Texas Chain Saw Massacre* and *Carrie*.

"Those movies told me fear was everything," Pruitt explains. "Fear was my brother. My sacred twin. My road to expanded consciousness."

According to Pruitt, "Death Rituals" is a combination of theater, horror film principles, real-life suffering, and radical method acting. Though the attraction treads some familiar ground, he insists that this is not a typical "walk-through" haunted house. "Once you enter the haunt, you will *become* these characters, and you will suffer and bleed just as they have. The ritual begins with your corruption—a transmogrification of your soul," he warns. "You can fight and kick and scream and try to survive—it will only make us work harder to destroy you."

Pruitt is well aware that extreme haunts can draw criticism and anger from the news media. During the protests over "The World of Horrors," people not only accused the producers of exploiting female victims of murder and abuse, they also began investigating the company's hiring practices, claiming that the actors in the haunt had not been properly trained. Rumors circulated that the haunt's owner, Roscoe Cahill, had even gone as far as to hire ex-felons to work as performers. Pruitt confesses that not all of these accusations were unfounded.

"That rumor about hiring ex-cons has some teeth," he explains as we enter the warehouse and begin stalking its cavernous halls. "At the time, I was just beginning volunteer work with a reentry program for ex-offenders in the state of Ohio, and I suggested that Roscoe look into the possibility of helping some of these men transition back into mainstream society. He was considering the idea when his cowardice took over and the project fell apart."

Now that Pruitt is in charge of his own haunt, he is committed to hiring those whom he believes deserve a second chance in life. However, he remains insistent that the actors receive extensive safety training and understand the intricacies of a live-action, full-contact haunt that relies heavily on psychological role-play and raw intensity. According to its creator, "Death Rituals" refuses to shy away from boundary-pushing themes, including murder, torture, bullying, and suicide. For reasons he refuses to clarify, Pruitt seems particularly drawn to the topic of self-sacrifice. "I'm fascinated by people who have the courage to punch their own ticket," he says.

As the counter-culture of extreme haunted houses continues to thrive in Southern California and elsewhere, Pruitt has improved his chances of success by surrounding himself with a team of investors, actors, and technicians who help bring his horrific visions to life. He explains that "Death Rituals" is more than just a haunted house or retro-grindhouse homage. As we exit the dark warehouse into the medicinal Los Angeles sunshine, he begins speaking about the importance of community when constructing participatory art. He refers to his investors and his production team as a family, a brotherhood, and that working together is "a communal experience for everyone involved."

As our interview comes to a close, Pruitt turns silent, guarded, as if our conversation has just broached subject matter that he wasn't ready to explore. His eyes remain hidden by his oversized sunglasses, and the raised scar on his throat throbs in the harsh sunlight. At the corner a Buick Regal idles behind a chain-link fence, waiting to pick him up. "If you want to be a part of history, then this is the place to be on Halloween—your black carriage, your divine escort," he says, pointing a crooked finger at the towering warehouse. "She will lie to you. She will trick you. But she will also anoint you and break you in like a fire and a hammer."

Uncompromising, unpredictable, and utterly terrifying, "Death Rituals" promises terror beyond belief—if only people will be brave enough to venture inside.

"DEATH RITUALS" HAUNTED ATTRACTION PRESS RELEASE

LOS ANGELES, CA (Fall, 2015) - From a mind born of bizarre cinematic horror comes a haunted attraction beyond the scope of your wildest imagination. Leave your inhibitions at the door and prepare to taste your fear. Will you run screaming for your life? Or will you die trying? This Halloween, face your inner demons in Bobby Pruitt's DEATH RITUALS, Southern California's newest experiment in psychological terror and depravity.

Located in the warehouse district of downtown Los Angeles, DEATH RITUALS features a multi-level haunt that puts you in the center of the bloody action. Each stage, or "ritual," of this nightmare world is based on the iconic horror films you know and love: Roger Spottiswoode's *Terror Train*, Tobe Hooper's *The Texas Chain Saw Massacre*, and Brian De Palma's *Carrie*.

Released in 1980 and starring original scream queen Jamie Lee Curtis, *Terror Train* boasts an atmospheric setting and practical special effects, but the film is most chilling in its opening scene of heartless bullying and one very rotted corpse. Relive this gruesome exposition in the psychosexual bedlam of DEATH RITUALS.

The ultimate celebration of cannibalistic bloodshed, Tobe Hooper's 1974 classic, *The Texas Chain Saw Massacre*, has often been cited as the most gut-wrenching horror movie of all time. Hooper's masterpiece cemented Leatherface and the rest of his demented clan as true icons of the genre. In a scene torn right from *Chain Saw* celluloid, DEATH RITUALS will force participants into having a "last supper" with this infamous gang of cannibal rejects. Come hungry for some hillbilly barbecue!

In 1976, Brian De Palma unveiled his dizzying interpretation of Stephen King's novel of telekinetic terror. A tale of teenage bullying, Christian fundamentalist quackery, and gory revenge, *Carrie* broke many cinematic taboos in its presentation of a magical feminine monster. In a sexually-charged climax not for the faint of heart, DEATH RITUALS gives you the chance to walk in the footsteps of

Carrie White herself, to undergo the tragedy and the pain and the mind-numbing sacrifice of a young girl on the brink of madness...

DEATH RITUALS takes place in a massive, three-story warehouse that has given creator Bobby Pruitt and his family of talented "fear architects" the chance to build an immersive world of horror-themed debauchery and chaos. Admission into the haunt includes not only the film-inspired adventures described above, but also an interactive, hallucinatory journey named CULT LAND, a Charles-Manson-fueled attraction that guides visitors through a virtual museum of torture and death. Those brave enough to enter DEATH RITUALS can spend time exploring the warehouse and all its macabre offerings, including a non-alcoholic bar that serves "Hitchcock's *Psycho* juice" and a gift shop stocked with t-shirts and stickers. And you never know who might be stalking these darkened halls, from serial killers to cult crazies, from suicide victims to elephant men, from sex-starved zombie nurses to insane voodoo tribesmen.

To enter DEATH RITUALS, all guests must be 18 or older with valid identification. Participants must fully read and sign a waiver before entering the premises—no exceptions. During DEATH RITUALS, guests will be touched, held, blindfolded, restrained with rope, and ordered to participate in the action. Many of the scenes inside DEATH RITUALS are of a violent, sexual, or aberrant nature. Guests are not allowed to touch or speak to the actors unless prompted. DEATH RITUALS features elements and effects that may not be appropriate for all audiences, including claustrophobic spaces, low lighting, artificial fog, pitch darkness, near-vertical stairs, strobe lights, physical contact, and full-frontal nudity. Please be aware that the attraction is not recommended for expecting mothers or for those with heart conditions. There is NO SAFE WORD and we recommend that participants wear clothes and shoes that can get wet, torn, or otherwise damaged.

DEATH RITUALS was founded and produced by Bobby Pruitt, a creative revolutionary in the uncompromising industry of immersive and extreme haunted attractions. Bobby was born and raised in the quiet riverboat town of Marietta, Ohio, where at an early age he developed a love of horror literature and film by browsing the bookshops and libraries of his neighborhood. As a boy, Bobby found companionship in fictional works such as Edgar Allan Poe's "The Fall of the House of Usher" and Henry James' *The Turn of the Screw*. As he grew older and fought the "black dog" of depression, his preferences turned toward darker and more controversial fare. Heavily influenced by long-time partner April Showers (the heavily-tattooed star of such trashy stage classics as *Naked Zombie Fuckers* and *The San Francisco Witch Killers*), Bobby became particularly interested in the low-budget exploitation films of the 1970s, including *The Last House on the Left*, *Snuff*, and *Faces of Death*. Prior to moving to Los Angeles, Bobby worked for Ohio's THE WORLD OF HORRORS, a controversial haunted attraction that remains one of the country's most daring and provocative attempts at merging the concept of the "haunted house" with real-life violence and true crime. In addition to bringing his ghastly visions to life in DEATH RITUALS, Bobby enjoys volunteering at the California Reentry Institute, a program that prepares male prisoners for the transition from incarceration to freedom, assisting them with housing and employment opportunities. A paradoxical showman, a counter-culture geek, and a haunted-house visionary, Bobby Pruitt looks forward to celebrating Halloween with those courageous enough to enter…DEATH RITUALS.

ORANGE COUNTY EXAMINER—A mixture of fringe theater and horror-film aesthetics, DEATH RITUALS will have most people wetting themselves in fear and disgust. In its effort to provide genuine chills and gory special effects, the haunted attraction succeeds on a grand scale, immersing customers in well-detailed sets from *Terror Train*, *The Texas Chain Saw Massacre*, and *Carrie*. But in order to experience these scenes ticket-holders must also endure acts of cruelty, humiliation, and punishment. They must confront graphic depictions of violence, death by suicide, and ritualistic murder...

Unlike most haunted houses, DEATH RITUALS relies on physical aggression to communicate most of its scares. You'll have to fend off various bad guys—including a steroid freak named "The Cannibal" and a smarmy piss-ant named "The Bully." Your best bet is to play along and let the actors to do their thing; the more you resist, the more they pile on the degradation (or the cockroaches). DEATH RITUALS is reckless and offensive, suited only for those willing to sink to its boggy depths and get *really* dirty...

HOLLYWOOD-GORE.COM—Building off of its controversial fanfare, DEATH RITUALS opened this weekend with solid crowds, drawing haunted-house veterans and curiosity seekers alike into its three-story chamber of madness. Fans of classics like Brian De Palma's *Carrie* and Tobe Hooper's *The Texas Chain Saw Massacre* will find much to love in this heady cocktail of immersive sets, theatrical effects, and no-holds-barred method acting...

The scares in DEATH RITUALS are almost all physical and psychologically disturbing. You will be touched. Groped. Pushed and shoved. Stinking of cheap booze and other putrid smells, the performers stalk each scene like monsters from your worst nightmares. To say any more would ruin all the fiendish surprises, but if the thought of crawling into bed with a naked chick covered in zits and blood doesn't get you all hot and bothered, you might just want to stay away...

PASADENA TRIBUNE—If you're looking for something wickedly inventive this Halloween season, look no further than the demented haunted attraction known as DEATH RITUALS. With custom-built set designs and shocking storylines that require guests to participate in the action, this unique experience caters to adults who want to be entertained, disturbed, and scared witless. Billed as the most extreme haunt in Southern California, DEATH RITUALS offers a mish-mash of cinematic terror and real-life chills that will have guests running, crawling, jumping, and screaming in fear. The acting is raw and out of control, keeping the nerves of the audience on edge, while the makeup and costume design reveal an impressive dedication to the craft. Not for the squeamish, this haunted house is all kinds of icky, but the visceral impact on its audience might just be worth the bouts of nausea...

CENTURY CITY NEWS—Ditch the plastic vampire fangs, fog machine, and spider-webs made out of cotton batting. DEATH RITUALS has come to Los Angeles and it intends to destroy the idea that a haunted house should be a fun and spooky experience...

Sexual depravity, simulated torture, and physical abuse all rear their ugly heads. So do humiliation and misogyny and the exploitation of real-life murder and suicide victims. The set design is cold and uninspired. The performers lumber about like child molesters at a schoolyard recess. This is not "interactive theater" or "participatory art." DEATH RITUALS is a sickening exercise in the dehumanization of the human spirit...

"Road Trip to Hell: College Students Say Haunted House Went Too Far" by Carson Richards (originally published in *Silicon Valley Online*, November, 2015, p. 2-4):

Three college students claim that an "extreme" haunted house in Southern California physically and emotionally abuses its guests to the point of injury and psychological distress.

"Death Rituals" opened in Los Angeles earlier this month, drawing large crowds due to its ubiquitous promotional campaign, graphic content, and high-volume scares. Everyone who enters the haunt must sign a waiver, part of which states that the actors will touch guests aggressively and may even leave scratches or bruising on their skin.

The attraction is produced by Bobby Pruitt, 37, who has written about the intensity of the experience in magazines and press releases. Described as an adults-only, full-contact haunted attraction, "Death Rituals" includes sexual themes and explicit subject matter, and guests may be bound, gagged, and placed in lurid and frightening situations.

Cherie Alvarez and Coral Harrington, both 18, and Paula Green, 20, bought tickets to "Death Rituals" after reading about the attraction on an online message board. On a road trip to Southern California, the women visited several other haunted attractions before attending "Death Rituals."

"It's all my fault," said Green, an aspiring actress and drama major. "I was the one who insisted we go. I thought it would be scary and fun, something that we could laugh about later. I didn't take what I read online seriously."

Green trembled as the painful memory of her experience in the haunted house played out in her mind. "What happened inside that house was disgusting. A violation of my body and my mind. I'll never forget it," she said.

On her online blog, Green described her experience inside "Death Rituals" in the following excerpted post:

...I am shoved into a room that stinks of piss and spilled booze. Bile rises in my throat. I don't know where my friends are. I don't know what I'm supposed to

do. Then a woman's voice— breathy and strained—tells me to "come closer." I step forward. Now I can see it—a four-poster bed draped in sheer curtains. The woman writhes in the sheets, groaning, and that terrible smell comes again, a wave of body odor and liquor. "Kitty," the woman croaks. "Here, kitty." And so I draw back one of the curtains to get a closer look, my heart hammering in my chest.

Her scream is an iron bolt to my brain, and before I can get away, she yanks me into the bed. The woman is naked, frail and bony and wet with blood. She mounts me, her body as dry as a husk, but her pubic hair sopping wet against my exposed skin. She pins my arms to the bed. Her face is covered in boils and cysts, and her long, greasy hair drags across my face, making it wet. Drool bubbles from her lips, her mouth flooded with spit. Only when I resist does she let me go and I'm up from the bed and scrambling for a way out.

I run to the other side of the room, looking for a door, when a wet sheet is wrapped around my head. I can't see. The sheet gets wrapped round and round, blinding me and filling my mouth. I start to panic. Rough hands begin pawing my neck. Someone lifts my shirt and roughly fingers my navel. My knees buckle and I fall down, tearing at the sheet until I pull it loose.

Men with flashlights have circled me. Some of them are rubbing their crotches. Others are laughing, clicking on and off their lights. Dizzy, I am pulled to my feet. A man begins describing my body in a booming voice—my face, the size of my breasts ("pink chewies," he calls them), my hips, my stomach. And then I'm pushed backward, hard, out of the room and into a corridor. I'm falling backward into a black, open space...

Alvarez and Harrington, who in the past have worked behind the scenes at haunted attractions, recalled their time inside "Death Rituals" with the same amount of anger and disgust.

Her face gripped with anguish, Alvarez described aggressive behavior from the actors, noting that they focused most of their violent attention on the female guests. According to the college freshman, she and Harrington were pushed, dragged, and verbally threatened inside the haunt. The threats included racial and sexual epithets, according to the two women.

"We signed the waiver, I get it, but this was a total glorification of violence against women," said Alvarez, who in high school was an active member of an anti-bullying organization. "I saw girls crying when they got out. One of them had her blouse ripped open. Another had broken blood vessels in her eye from being slapped across the face."

Harrington said that at one point during the haunt, an actor tied her hands to a chair made out of animal bones and forced her to eat "slop" from a dirty bowl. "It was dangerous. People were getting hit and choked, and they had trouble breathing," she said.

"If you're overweight or have some kind of physical defect in their eyes, they body-shame you and taunt you even more," Harrington continued.

In a recent interview with *Haunt America*, a magazine about the haunt industry, Pruitt argued that his attraction employs "the illusion of horror." Overwhelmed by the lifelike depictions of gore and bloodshed, guests come to believe they are the victims of real violence themselves. In reality, Pruitt claimed, the haunt is entirely safe.

"The truth is, my guests only *think* something has happened to them," Pruitt was quoted as saying. "It's all parlor tricks, optical illusions, psychological poetry—everything else is just backstabbing and outright lies."

In addition to calling Pruitt a "liar and a sadist," Alvarez said that she found other parts of the haunted attraction disturbing as well, including an emphasis on real-life suicide victims and the exploitation of people with physical abnormalities.

"The horror genre explores the dark side of our society, the things we don't understand or that make us afraid," she said. "But I think most people want to be entertained rather than grossed out, abused, or mocked for being different. The haunted house wasn't scary—it was *cruel*, and more people should know about what they're agreeing to before they go inside."

Although attendance at "Death Rituals" was initially strong, online reports indicate that interest in the haunt has tapered off as more and more negative reactions have been posted on the Internet and in newspapers and magazines. Despite the critical backlash and the accusations of assault, Pruitt has plans to produce similar types of horror-themed events throughout the year.

COMMENTS:

Junipero
3 hours ago

I've been working in haunted attractions since I was a teenager and the changes I've seen in the industry in the past few years make me angry and sad. "Death Rituals" isn't a haunted house. It's a torture chamber! Bobby Pruitt rips off ideas from classic horror movies and disguises his lack of creativity behind buckets of fake blood and a confusing waiver that people are forced to read in the dark. I'm glad these girls spoke out and are working to put a stop to this.

TruthSeeker
2 hours ago

Let me get this straight. Three bubble-headed college chicks pay to go to a haunted house, and then complain that it scared them? I've been to every haunted attraction in L.A., and they're all the same. A bunch of stupid jump scares and rinky-dink effects. At least Pruitt's trying to do something different. And yeah, sometimes you get touched! Big deal! These girls signed a waiver and knew exactly what they were getting into. A perfect example of how feminism turns gullible women into victims.

Halloween1978
2 hours ago

Hold on, TruthSeeker. I go to a lot of haunted houses too, and there's a big difference between jump scares, stalking someone in line, touching their shoulder or grabbing their hand, and what goes on at "Death Rituals." Waiver or not, don't make excuses for sickos who get off on watching young women suffer and cry. Unless you're a sicko yourself?

SlasherSmile2000
1 hour ago

Paula Green openly admitted that they had read about "Death Rituals" online and made the choice to go. Sounds a bit sketch. That's like watching an R-rated movie and then complaining it was too violent or dropped too many F-bombs. These girls seem a bit entitled to me.

Haunted
45 min ago

Of course there's no mention of any abuse men might have suffered in the haunt. Nope, just the women. I find it hard to believe that they would target only the female guests. What are the guys doing the whole time? Standing around and watching, like some sort of sick bachelor party? The story doesn't make sense.

Majestic
40 min ago

Haunted, I went through the snake-pit that is "Death Rituals," and my experience is nearly identical to the one these women talk about (if not worse). My boyfriend didn't get half the crap I got. Also, you should know that Bobby Pruitt has a history of hiring ex-cons to work for him as actors. They could be robbers or drug dealers. Rapists or murderers. I have connections in the industry and I'm telling all my friends to boycott this dump.

Stowaway32
35 min ago

Yeah, Haunted, because men never get together in groups and watch women being degraded and humiliated. I guess you've never heard of strip clubs and porno theaters.

NormanBates

20 min ago

If I were any of you, I'd shut your mouths. People are watching these message boards.

Bennington

5 min ago

I'm the co-producer of a "haunters" convention in Reno and would like to arrange a panel about extreme haunts for our upcoming event in winter. If you've participated in "Death Rituals" or any other extreme haunt and have something to say, click on my name and email me.

KingJames

3 min ago

A message for Mr. Pruitt: "Woe to the wicked! It shall be ill with him, for what his hands have dealt out shall be done to him." –Isaiah 3:11

Majestic

Just now

I'm drawing up a petition right now about putting a stop to "Death Rituals." For anyone shocked and angered by the article above, I hope you'll sign it. Stay tuned.

From "Extreme Haunt Producers and Survivors: Welcome to the New Halloween" moderated by Janice Powers and transcribed by Phil Bennington (*Haunters Convention and Tradeshow*, Reno, Nevada, Winter, 2015):

THE FOLLOWING EXCERPTED TRANSCRIPT IS FROM A LIVE PANEL DISCUSSION AND HAS BEEN EDITED FOR EASE OF READING. EVERY EFFORT WAS MADE TO KEEP THIS TEXT TRUE TO EACH SPEAKER'S ORIGINAL MEANING AND INTENT.

JANICE POWERS (host): Now that the 2015 Halloween season has officially wrapped, we have a special discussion for our guests here at the 6th annual Haunters Convention and Tradeshow. From neighborhood fright-fests to large-scale attractions inside your local shopping mall, haunted houses are more popular now than ever before. Onstage we'll be speaking with Daniel Ritter, the creative director behind "The Devil's Business: Manson's House of Blood"; Mark D'Angelo, executive producer of "Execution"; Cherie Alvarez and Coral Harrington, survivors of "Death Rituals," a contentious haunt out of Southern California; and Sonya Cox, an actress who has performed in haunted attractions throughout the state of Nevada.

I'm sure our discussion will cover a lot of ground, but I want to focus on immersive haunted houses—the merging of a haunted attraction with role-playing, interactive theater, and controversial performance art—and what some people call "extreme." Before we get started, let's watch some video footage from "The Devil's Business: Manson's House of Blood."

ON PROJECTION SCREEN: *A grainy, hand-held film showing a YOUNG WOMAN, 20s, sitting on a couch in a dark room. Her hands are tied with a lamp cord, her mouth stuffed with an oily dishrag. The woman looks exhausted, heavy bags under her eyes, makeup and eyeliner smeared across her face. An OLDER MAN, late 30s and dressed in bohemian clothing, enters the frame. He sticks his tongue out at the camera before turning to the young woman.*

The man says something into the woman's ear, but the film is silent and without subtitles. The woman tries to scoot away from the man but he grabs her forcefully by the hair and yanks her body close to his. The man begins to kiss the woman's ear, sucking the earlobe and tugging on it with his teeth. The woman starts to cry. The man laughs at the camera, wiggling his tongue. He then produces a pillowcase and forcibly covers the young woman's head with it.

The camera follows the man to a long table covered in a plastic sheet. Spread out on the table are two knives and a carving fork. Painted in red on the wall behind the table are the words DEATH TO PIGS and HELTER SKELTER. The man runs his finger along the tines of the carving fork before picking it up. The film cuts to black.

The following words appear in white block letters: "I am whoever you make me, but what you want is a fiend; you want a sadistic fiend because that is what you are."

POWERS: On that horrific note, Daniel, let's start with you! Some people say that "The Devil's Business: Manson's House of Blood" straddles that fine line between a traditional haunted house and the exploitation of real-life murder victims. The video footage we just watched gives us only a glimpse of what the attraction has to offer. What more can you tell us about your new and controversial haunt experience?

DANIEL RITTER (creative director): Before I talk about "Manson's House of Blood," it's important to go back to the beginning of my career in horror entertainment. I've been involved in the haunt industry for over 25 years. I started with small residential haunted houses and volunteer-based fundraisers that brought much-needed resources to my community. There wasn't any profit involved and nearly all of the scares were "jump-scares."

My first official haunted house opened in 2001. It had a serial killer theme and was based on Jack the Ripper. The crew was made up of my friends and family, and we dealt with every possible issue you could imagine—from the actors to the construction, from the legal permits to the marketing and overall operation of the business—we handled every detail. And all of this was going on while I was running a used bookstore and part-timing at my local library.

From there we just expanded. We found more actors, set designers, and crew managers. We found an awesome publicist and two of the best makeup artists in the industry. We found bigger properties where we could host our attractions. And most of all, we found a loyal audience. I belonged to a book club that focused on true-crime literature, and I started implementing more of these non-fiction stories into our haunts. Now we employ a large team of artists and creative individuals who work together to provide the most powerful and memorable experience possible. "The Devil's Business: Manson's House of Blood" is the first haunted attraction based on the Manson Murders. It's extreme, filled with gory special effects, audience participation, and other nasty things—but there are also elements of morbid humor and fantasy.

POWERS: Now, Mark, you're doing something a bit different than Daniel and his team. You've centered your attraction around the theme of capital punishment. Tell us about "Execution."

MARK D'ANGELO (executive producer): There are a lot of influences behind "Execution," like *Tales from the Crypt*, the Salem Witchcraft Trials, and those torture and inquisition museums scattered throughout Europe. Right now we're operating out of New York and Los Angeles, but we hope to expand to other cities if we can find the right locations. "Execution" needs a space with an open floor plan that can house several different exhibits and scenes at one time. But the interactive aspects of attraction require big rooms with proper drainage systems, hidden doorways, and moveable walls—so it takes a large building that can handle all that stuff.

POWERS: Mark, your inspirations for "Execution" include elements from our nation's dark past. And, Daniel, you're pulling from history too, with an emphasis on the most infamous murder in the entire world. Was this a conscious way of distancing yourself from commercial haunted attractions?

D'ANGELO: Our crew takes their inspirations from just about everywhere—books, comics, movies, video games, and history. We're marketing our product to a diverse audience, so we try to dip into every genre pool to appeal to a broad crowd. One of our scenes features a real medieval torture device called the "Pear of Anguish," which lawmen inserted into the orifices of a prisoner to stretch open his skin. At the same time, we have exhibitions inspired by the *Saw* and *Hostel* movies, and one of our extreme sequences mirrors a scene from *Men Behind the Sun*, a film about Japanese war crimes during World War II. Our guests want to relate to what they see in our haunt, and we try to provide that through an intensely visceral experience.

RITTER: It was definitely our goal to distance ourselves from the norm. In some of our earlier houses, we avoided being overly graphic or violent but, as Mark alluded to, our customers want more intensity and direct interaction with every passing season. We use a real-life narrative in "Manson's House of Blood," filled with historical ephemera, visual cues, and film montages. Most of our guests were raised on the Internet and the concept of instantaneous stimulation. The extreme nature of the haunt is a natural extension of that deep, sensory interaction that so many haunted house fans crave today.

POWERS: I want to talk more about that—extreme haunted houses and the themes that embody them. But first, let's turn to our other guests and get their input on some of the topics we've addressed so far. Cherie and Coral, I'd like to start with you. My producer, Phil Bennington, actually got a hold of you both after he read an article about your experience with Bobby Pruitt's "Death Rituals," an extreme haunted house in L.A. Before we get to all that went down there, I'd like to start out with a simpler question. When you were children, what scared you the most?

CORAL HARRINGTON (student): I had an overactive imagination as a kid, so everything from monster cartoons to Stephen King books terrified me. But I love getting scared! The adrenaline rush, that rollercoaster-drop feeling in the pit of your stomach when something really freaks you out. The *Paranormal Activity* series affected me that way. I saw the first one when I was around 11, and that movie became a permanent fixture in my nightmares.

CHERIE ALVAREZ (student): For me it was "domestic horror"—anything having to do with killers or supernatural entities invading someone's home and murdering them. My father has an interesting psychological point of view on this. He thinks I use horror movies and haunted houses as a way to cope with the fears of my childhood. When I was younger, we watched movies like *Tamara*, which is about a girl who returns from the dead to kill her bullies. We watched *Carrie* and *Dark Night of the Scarecrow*. Our discussions would make me less scared, but they also helped me understand tragedy and victimhood in different ways.

POWERS: I'd like to build off of what Daniel said earlier about the extreme nature of some haunted houses and tie that to Cherie and Coral's insight into victimhood. Daniel, I know there's a certain amount of secrecy with an attraction like yours, but can you give us a few examples of how "Manson's House of Blood" fits into the "extreme" category?

RITTER: We tie people up with rope—the same way the victims in the Manson Murders were tied up. We seal their mouths with duct tape, threaten them with real knives and guns, and use ultrasonic headphones to fill their ears with sounds of human torture and dismemberment. At the Sharon Tate crime scene, the killers draped nylon rope over a ceiling beam, possibly to hang the victims, so we've simulated a hanging—like a "forced" suicide.

POWERS: Let's introduce Sonya Cox, an actress who has performed in haunted attractions for many years here in Nevada. Welcome to the panel, Sonya. Just now, as you listened to Daniel describe what goes on at his attraction, you had a visible reaction. Have you ever performed in an extreme haunted house?

SONYA COX (actress): I've worked for many different haunts, from the big productions at Aces Ballpark to low-key attractions in downtown Reno. But no, I've never performed in an extreme haunt. Speaking frankly, I never would.

POWERS: And why is that?

COX: I don't want to offend Daniel or Mark, but I don't think their events should be called haunted attractions. I understand that there are no hard and fast rules to this sort of thing, but a line has to be drawn somewhere between safe Halloween entertainment and legalized torture where people, mostly young women, are being verbally abused and physically injured. I mean, we all saw the video that Daniel brought with him. My heart breaks for that poor girl. I would question any haunted house that requires its customers to sign a lengthy waiver filled with confusing legal jargon.

POWERS: But we must ask—is it actual physical abuse? What distinctions can we make between a haunted house that involves physical interaction—such as Reno's "Slaughterhouse Junction," which Sonya *has* performed in—and attractions that are so extreme that people are leaving them distraught, crying, and with scrapes and bruises on their bodies? I want to hear from Cherie and Coral. We invited them to our event because they can speak directly to their experience inside a notorious haunt—"Death Rituals." Even the name of the attraction implies a certain level of extremity. Cherie and Coral, how did you not know what you were getting into?

ALVAREZ: We get asked that question a lot, and it's a fair one. We have never denied signing the waiver for "Death Rituals," and I can tell you—we actually read it. They do whatever they can to make sure you *don't* read it—

HARRINGTON: Yeah, you're outside, in the dark, when they shove the waiver in your face with a pen. The print is small, and there's no light to read it. We actually took the paper across the street where there was a streetlamp. One of their security guys yelled at us because we had taken a legal document off the property.

ALVAREZ: We knew we were going into an extreme experience. We understood we might be tied up or confined. We anticipated the fake blood, disturbing imagery, and violent scenes. But the waiver doesn't tell you that "Death. Rituals" includes conditions that are dangerous and unsanitary. It doesn't tell you that you'll leave with cuts and bruises. It doesn't tell you that the actors get genuine pleasure out of torturing and hurting women, or that gang rape is a prevailing theme. It doesn't tell you that in their haunt the word "no" really means "yes," and that doing things against your will is the only way they're going to let you out.

POWERS: Coral, were you forced to do things against your will in "Death Rituals"?

HARRINGTON: Absolutely. Inside the haunt, there's a dinner scene based on *The Texas Chain Saw Massacre*, and they tie you up and put bowls of slop in front of you and make you eat it. Not a small bowl either, but a large one, filled to the brim. We can't say for sure, as no one from their production office will respond to our phone calls and emails, but most people who have gone through the haunt agree that the slop is dog food. *Real* dog food. Pet food isn't subjected to the same health and safety regulations that human food is. Commercial dog food contains intestines, slaughterhouse waste, and poisonous chemicals. I was forced to ingest several spoonfuls of it before I was allowed to the last part of the haunt and get out of there, and I was sick for three days afterward.

POWERS: When you say you were "forced"—couldn't you just walk out? Just get up and leave?

HARRINGTON: No. I was tied up. And I was told explicitly that I was not going to be let out of the building unless I ate what was in the bowl. The girl next to me actually vomited onto the table.

POWERS: And you had another friend with you, correct? Paula Green? In response to my letter, she told me that she had been bound with zip-ties inside the haunt. That she had been spat on and was forced to put her head inside a soiled pair of underwear. That a character known as "The Bully" pushed her onto the floor and called her, and I'm quoting directly from Paula's email here, an "anorexic cunt." I have to admit—I find this repulsive.

CHERIE: And that's not even the worst of it.

POWERS: Now, Cherie, you've gone on record about not only the injuries you received at "Death Rituals"—a scratched face, bruising in your chest area, scrapes on your hands—but also about injuries you saw other men and women suffer. You've started to document these occurrences, is that right?

ALVAREZ: I have. I'm a psychology major, and I plan to write a research paper about extreme haunts and the aftermath of going through them. I've seen men forced to strip naked. Women coming out with swollen and discolored faces, their clothes torn and their undergarments exposed. Some people are crying—hysterical. At the very least, I want people to understand what they are signing up for. I don't want to get on a pedestal—or, hell, maybe I do—but in "Death Rituals," there's a point where sickness and depravity become so severe, the pendulum of decency swings in such the opposite direction, that someone has to stand up and put a stop to it.

POWERS: I'm not ignoring the significance of your physical injuries, but I hope you don't mind me asking—have either of you experienced any long-term effects from participating in "Death Rituals"? I have online messages here in front of me from people that say they now suffer from PTSD and other afflictions after going through an extreme haunted house.

HARRINGTON: I now have nightmares. They've affected my education and my personal relationships. A few times I've woken up with a fright, thinking that one of the actors from the haunt is standing over my bed, or trying to climb in bed with me.

ALVAREZ: For me, it's a trust issue. I've always been wary of strangers and people in large groups—but I was getting better. I was growing more confident in myself, learning to accept myself, especially since starting college and being around more like-minded people. But this experience has made me less trusting of others. I've become less friendly, and I've always been a friendly person. It's *triggered* something inside me. I don't know how else to describe it.

POWERS: Now, I think we should make it clear that neither of you has participated in "Manson's House of Blood" or "Execution."

ALVAREZ: That's right.

POWERS: And that we offered Bobby Pruitt the opportunity to participate on this panel, and he refused. To quote directly from his email, he told us to go "fuck ourselves."

HARRINGTON: That's because he knew he'd get his ass kicked if he showed up.

POWERS: But he did send us a series of photographs depicting various scenes from "Death Rituals." Let's take a look at those now.

ON PROJECTION SCREEN: *The more graphic images are censored by red masking tape. The pictures include a SCREAMING WOMAN tied to a chair made of animal bones; a BALDING MAN stripped to his undershorts, his face smeared with brown slop; a TATTOOED WOMAN clutching a bottle of booze, her skin covered in lesions; a COCKROACH feasting on a piece of moldy bread; the torso of a NAKED WOMAN, her breasts scratched and bleeding, the nipples poked through with sewing needles; a BLOODY MATTRESS covered in straight razors.*

POWERS: On the one hand, it's hard to look at these pictures. I can't help but feel we are seeing something that we are not supposed to see. And yet, at the same time, I can't look away. Bobby Pruitt is daring us to look death in the eye and to determine our own moral barometer when it comes to horror. Cherie, are you outraged by these images?

ALVAREZ: Listen, Coral and I are not here to condemn all extreme haunts. We never intended to become spokespersons for some kind of anti-haunted-house movement. I mean, we love Halloween, horror movies, and scary books. Last year we wrote an interactive horror play called *The Satanist*, and that story had pieces of things that we learned from going to haunted houses like the ones Daniel and Mark are talking about. But as a woman—and as a survivor of tragedy—there are certain places I don't think our society needs to go. An event like "Death Rituals" is one of them, and that's why we're here.

POWERS: We have so much more to talk about, and we want to take questions from our audience, too—but Daniel, you seem to be champing at the bit here. What would you like to say about what Cherie and Coral have spoken about tonight?

RITTER: Well, I can't address their experiences directly. "Death Rituals" isn't my haunt and I've never met Bobby Pruitt. But I will say this. In our haunted attraction, we rough you up. We put you through your paces. But people aren't being beaten and they're not being tortured. You're going to get pushed around. Pinched, punched—whatever. Some of the interaction between our actors and guests is of a violent and sexual nature, but it's *fiction*. They *volunteer* for this shit. It's the same thing as going to a horror movie—well, *almost* the same thing. And even Cherie admits—she *loves* those! Our haunt is going to *scare* you. That's what you're paying us to do. It's not illegal, what we're doing—I want to make that clear. If anything, we're being more realistic about the state of the world today than some sanitized horror play in a college theater. If you don't like it, don't buy a ticket. The rest us can have all the fun we want without being judged by the people who don't get it.

ALVAREZ: By writing that play, we were trying to show that just because you've put the most disgusting scenes possible into your haunted house does not mean you've created good horror.

RITTER: But who's to say what constitutes good horror? You? You're only 19, for Christ's sake. You weren't even born when *The Exorcist* or *Texas Chain Saw* came out. Or *Poltergeist*. Hell, even fuckin' *Ghostbusters*!

HARRINGTON: You don't have to be an asshole, dude.

POWERS: And I think that's a good place to stop before we take questions from our audience. Again, I want to thank our panel for being here tonight for this rather heated debate. Extreme haunted attractions—healthy Halloween entertainment or exploitative garbage? You be the judge here at the 6th annual Haunters Convention and Tradeshow...

"Professional Ethics in Extreme Haunted Attractions" by Cherie Alvarez (a research paper written for Social Psychology, BC1137, Winter, 2015):

"Extreme" haunted attractions eschew traditional "jump" scares and "pop-up" ghosts in favor of immersive experiences that involve violence, torture, and psychosexual situations. Due to the controversial nature of this rising trend in the haunt industry, these attractions pose ethical challenges to their practitioners. This paper will examine three facets of extreme haunted houses—interpretation, narrative, and ethics—and the ways these facets are addressed by two companies offering a form of entertainment that Bethany Treadwell (2013) has called "a hands-on nightmare of misogyny, bullying, and psychological shaming" (p. 2).

The popularity of extreme haunted houses "hinges on our macabre fascination with death and our willingness to look true horror in the eyes" (Treadwell, 2015, p. 2). While many haunted attractions focus on paranormal or apocalyptic terror, extreme haunts capitalize on genuine human suffering and, in unique cases, merge real-life events with the narratives and tropes of the horror film. This paper uses research, interviews, and anecdotal evidence[1] to explore how the producers of extreme haunted houses interpret the genre and how they adhere to professional ethics. These issues will be studied in a comparative examination of two specific extreme haunts: Christopher Andersen's "The Underground" and Bobby Pruitt's "Death Rituals."

---

[1] My interviews with participants in "The Underground" and "Death Rituals" were confidential, and the names of these interviewees have been withheld by mutual agreement. All interviews were digitally recorded and faithfully transcribed. I conducted a phone interview with Christopher Andersen, while all quotes attributed to Bobby Pruitt are taken from *Haunted America* and *Haunter's Realm* (September, October, 2013).

Extreme Haunt Literature and Previous Studies

Martinez and Holt (2011) were arguably the first contributors to literature on extreme haunts, though their work focused primarily on summarizing the haunt narratives—if any existed—and providing colorful descriptions of certain scenes or characters. While Martinez and Holt did much to add legitimacy to the few extreme attractions in existence in 2011, more recent studies have been devoted to the creation, marketing, and tone of extreme haunted attractions, especially those in California. For example, Hendrickson (2013) studied the museum-like set design of "Lights Off," an art installation/haunted house located in a Los Angeles theater; and "Execution," which Hendrickson called "a surprisingly effective depiction of what it might be like to witness real-life capital punishment" (p. 8).

"Real-life" extreme haunts refer primarily to attractions that use true crimes or events as inspiration for narrative, setting, and character. Controversial, these attractions are often situated in mock-ups of infamous crime-scene locations, including the house formerly at 10050 Cielo Drive (the site of the Manson Murders). Keager (2013) defined participation in "real-life" extreme haunts as "a tremulous, if not dangerous, balance between play-acting and raw terror" (p. 13). She added that those who produce this genre of haunt "must consider the ethical and legal ramifications of their product" (p. 15). Williams (2013) agreed with Keager's assessment in his case study of the production struggles and collapse of "The World of Horrors," a haunt that had intended to depict scenes from a fictional "snuff" film and give participants the opportunity to participate in the simulated murder of a teenage girl. Williams argued, "Unlike most haunts that follow a linear walk-through format, 'The World of Horrors' was asking participants to make choices that impacted the narrative and altered the physical space and performances of the actors...an intriguing idea, if only the producers had been willing to distance their project from extreme sexual violence and ritualistic abuse" (p. 18). Williams added that the "questionable hiring practices and the dubious motives of the actors" made the undertaking of "The World of Horrors" a "financial, logistical, and managerial nightmare" (p. 18).

The psychological motivation to participate in extreme haunted attractions has generated considerable press in magazines and news articles about the haunt industry. When visitors enter a traditional haunted house, they know they will be following a fixed path (often marked by visual cues, like arrows and sign-posts), that any verbal threats against them pose no real danger, and that the performers are forbidden from touching the participants. In addition, anecdotal evidence from Keager (2013) indicates that a significant psychological draw to these haunts is the anticipation of the experience itself, often magnified by waiting in line in the dark and being playfully "attacked" by "clowns, zombies, vampires, and other creatures" (p. 7). But participation in extreme haunted attractions stems from a more deep-rooted psychological place, according to Williams (2013). Some people might partake in an extreme haunt in order to "reach beyond ordinary life and test emotional limits" (Williams, 2013, p. 20). Others "may have something to prove and a desire to stop living in fear" (Williams, 2013, p. 20). Keager defined this longing as a "dangerous interpretation of the primitive fight-or-flight survival mechanism through which people—many of whom sign the waiver form without reading it—subject themselves to legal torture" (p. 15). Ultimately, as Pickford (2014) argued in "Hermetic Space in Haunted Attractions," haunted houses should be enjoyed as a form of "seasonal entertainment that transposes negative emotions, including fear and mistrust, into pleasurable experiences" (p. 10). However, the fact that some extreme haunted attractions integrate real-life tragedies into their narratives raises concerns about exploitation, ethics, and the safety of the customers.

Extreme Haunted Houses: "The Underground" and "Death Rituals"

Leland (2014) examined the horror trope of the "live burial" as a popular feature in many haunted attractions, including Christopher

Andersen's "The Underground," an immersive burial simulator in San Francisco. Through personal interviews, Leland learned that the majority of participants, while lying in a real coffin outfitted with pistons and sensory stimuli, felt a "mixture of panic and claustrophobia," but also that "their safety was never truly at risk" (p. 4). Leland classified "The Underground" as an extreme haunt due to the "solitary nature of the experience, the sensory deprivation, and the aggressive physical interaction between the customer and the crypt-keeper, a giant man wearing a mask and leather smock" (p. 2). However, most participants reported that they enjoyed the experience and some happily posed for pictures with the crypt-keeper afterward (Leland, 2014, p. 3). In stark contrast, Bobby Pruitt's "Death Rituals," despite a promotional campaign that promised ticket-holders the opportunity to "act out scenes from [their] favorite horror movies," has received largely negative press, the most damning being first-person accounts from those who were allegedly "bullied, groped, and assaulted" during the experience (Sanders, 2015, p. 22). Pruitt's attraction, which opened in a three-story Los Angeles warehouse in 2015, has also been accused of exploiting serious social problems (e.g. bullying, self-harm, suicide) and real human tragedy.

Though these haunts were selected primarily for their content, their geographical locations are worth noting. San Francisco and Los Angeles have a history of violent crime, including serial murder. Just a mile and a half from the notorious federal prison known as Alcatraz, and home of the unsolved "Zodiac" killings in the late 1960s and early 1970s, San Francisco has become a recent hotbed for producers of extreme haunted houses. According to Leland (2014), "from the mafia syndicates of the 1930s to legends of barroom ghosts and back-alley spirits, death permeates the city by the bay" (pg. 1) Leland also noted that San Francisco currently offers a number of haunted attractions during Halloween season, among them extreme haunts, ghost tours, and interactive theater. Los Angeles has also had its share of human tragedy brought on by violent crime, including the Black Dahlia killing in 1947, the Manson Murders in 1969, and the "Night Stalker" serial slayings in the mid-80s. In a pictorial map, Leland (2014) highlighted other important sites located throughout the city—including the Wonderland Murders House, the Cecil Hotel, and the Queen Mary ocean liner—that have served as locations of or inspirations for haunted houses throughout Southern California.

Archetypal Features and Interpretation of Extreme Haunts

Unlike most haunted attractions that accommodate as many guests as possible over the course of several hours, both Andersen and Pruitt emphasize the importance of an isolated experience in their haunts. Due to its hermetic space and live-burial theme, "The Underground" hosts one visitor at a time. The haunt lasts anywhere from 2 to 6 minutes, depending on whether or not the participant uses the safe word. "The first part of the haunt is the customer's interaction with the crypt-keeper. He's cursing at them and shoving them. He's very aggressive before they get inside the tomb," Andersen says. "But participants know that there's an intercom in the coffin, and we can hear them if they use the safe word." Similarly, Pruitt allows no more than eight customers to walk through "Death Rituals" at one time. "I run an immersive, full-contact haunt with no safe word," says Pruitt. "The whole point is to experience isolated terror that is brought on by being the victim of cruelty and violence." Pruitt's attraction—which features scenes inspired by the horror movies *The Texas Chain Saw Massacre* (1974), *Carrie* (1976), and *Terror Train* (1980)—lasts 45 minutes. Like most extreme haunts, "The Underground" and "Death Rituals" require customers to sign a waiver before entering the attraction. If customers do not follow the rules stated in the waiver, they are asked to leave the haunt, forfeiting the cost of the ticket and their right to participate in the event.

Keager (2013) stated that traditional haunted attractions, usually those located at theme parks or private residences, allow for groups of up to four or five participants at one time who follow a "guided route" through the haunt (p. 12). These haunts typically feature animatronics and figures, actors reciting lines of rehearsed dialogue while dressed in thematic costumes, and various audio and sensory effects like music, fan-generated wind, or heated air (Keager, 2013, p. 12). Keager adds that, more often than not, "a man wearing a mask and wielding a buzzing (chainless) chainsaw chases a group of screaming kids out the exit to end the haunt" (p. 13). Some traditional haunted houses will include a narrative based around a horror theme, but the "stories are paper-thin, barely distinguishable once visitors begin the walk-through" (Keager, 2013, p. 13). While "The Underground" and "Death Rituals" avoid many of these archetypal elements, Andersen admits that "The Underground" is "light on story, but heavy on mood and tone." Pruitt, on the other hand, considers the narrative in "Death Rituals" to be critical to the physical and psychological terror of the experience. In "Death Rituals," participants assume the roles of famous characters from a selection of horror films of the 1970s and 80s. "We give you costumes to wear, we play music from the movies, we blindfold you and disorient you and play games with your head and body—anything we can do to turn your mind upside down and your flesh inside out," Pruitt says.

But the derivative "plot" of "Death Rituals" is not the only element of the haunt that separates it from traditional haunted attractions. Keager (2013) explains that a major stipulation in most traditional haunted houses—especially the "brand-name commercial attractions at theme parks"—states that the actors cannot touch the participants (p. 9). While the crypt-keeper from "The Underground" physically interacts with participants, the results are relatively tame, at least within the world of extreme haunts: guests were observed getting pushed or grabbed; two men had their caps thrown to the ground and stomped on; and another woman began to cry after the crypt-keeper pulled her arm and shouted profanities at her (C. Alvarez, observation, October 15, 2015). On a psychological and physical level, the actors from "Death Rituals" get far more involved with the participants, as described later in this paper. "My attraction is a direct response to the candy-coated principles of most corporate haunted houses in the industry," Pruitt says. "'Death Rituals' forces you to face your darkest, most primitive fears and desires. It is a place of sickness and disease, a place where people test the boundaries of their ability to endure pain and suffering."

Another primary feature of all haunted attractions—traditional and extreme—is the exploitation of our fear of the dark. Many traditional haunted houses capitalize on this fear by beginning with a brief stretch of total darkness that finds visitors groping blindly along to find the correct path, sometimes with the aid of a cheap flashlight. Leland (2014) stated that darkness "reminds people of death" and can often cause "anxiety, panic attacks, and feelings of claustrophobia" (p. 11). Rarely do traditional haunted attractions generate such extreme reactions. However, the same cannot be said for extreme haunts. The burial simulator in Andersen's "The Underground" plunges customers into a dark and hermetic space. Coupled with the use of frightening sounds and a real casket, the haunt can often cause anxiety and true panic. "I thought it might be a way to conquer my fear of enclosed spaces," one participant said. "But it was awful. The coffin was locked and I started to hyperventilate." The first set-piece of Pruitt's "Death Rituals"—an emulation of the opening scene of *Terror Train*, in which a bullied college student is traumatized by a prank involving a woman's corpse—also relies on total darkness. On their way to the room where the rotting "body" lies in wait, customers must crawl through a dark, tunnel-like hallway while being groped by unseen hands that emerge through holes in the wall. Though Pruitt argues that the tunnel sequence serves to "amplify the nervous tension" before the haunt really gets underway, one customer stated that the "holes are cut very low in the wall so that the actors can grab and fondle you underneath."

At this juncture, it is important to note that customers who participate in extreme haunted houses are doing so of their own volition. Treadwell (2013) stated that participants in extreme haunts consider themselves "horror veterans, bored with the traditional fare that the spooky season has to offer and searching for something intense, even dangerous" (p. 10). For this reason, Andersen argues, haunted house companies must continually find ways to appeal to customers looking for "the next rush of dopamine," and to promote their businesses in order to turn a profit.

The Narratives of Extreme Haunts

Haunted house companies (and haunted house enthusiasts who design and operate haunted houses in residential neighborhoods) use different marketing strategies to draw audiences to their attractions, including interactive websites, flyers, postcards, and advertisements and coupons in community newspapers and industry magazines like *Haunted America* (Martinez and Holt, 2011, p. 3). Attempting to strike an ethical balance between creating seasonal entertainment and avoiding exploitation, producers of extreme haunts have come under fire for some of their promotional tactics. Ohio's "The World of Horrors," the interactive haunt that was partly designed to replicate a snuff film, employed marketing techniques that seemed to celebrate the exploitation of real-life tragedy—among them, "flyers featuring pictures of real abducted or murdered women" (Williams, 2013, p. 11). According to the haunt's press release, the producers of the attraction also planned to capture each simulated murder on film and make the footage available to watch on a private website. But with just weeks to go before its opening in 2014, the "snuff" haunt was preemptively closed due to legal pressure from victim advocacy groups throughout the country. Bobby Pruitt, who worked as lead set designer on the haunt, was quoted as saying, "A pit bull with buckshot in its belly still has teeth to bite you with. You shut me down, I'll just strike back harder and louder the next time—and all you man-haters and cowards will regret it."

Indeed, the commercial failure of "The World of Horrors" has not stopped producers from pursuing the extreme-haunt genre and using real-life tragedy and serious social issues to build their narratives. Though Christopher Andersen's "The Underground" lacks any sort of cohesive storyline to construct the simulation of being buried alive, customers are exposed to a notorious true crime as part of the experience. Performed by a voice actor and broadcast through speakers as guests wait in line, the story of the abduction and imprisonment of Colleen Stan in 1977 is one of the most horrific cases of sexual violence in American history. In between bouts of rape and torture, Stan's abductors forced the 20-year-old to live in a coffin-like box for nearly 7 years. Stan eventually escaped and one of her tormentors now rots in state prison—but Andersen's narrative, delivered in a dramatic baritone voice worthy of Vincent Price, leaves these details out. "I've been accused of exploiting Colleen Stan, a real person alive today, and sensationalizing violence," Andersen says. "But that's not my intent. Extreme haunts help us to redefine our value system. Going through a burial simulation helps people to have a greater appreciation for life." Although Andersen uses the tragedy of Colleen Stan to set a frightful tone and provide a tenuous link to being buried in a coffin, all semblance of narrative disappears once the live burial simulation begins. The fact that the story of Colleen Stan plays a small role in the haunt does not excuse Andersen from exploiting her suffering for entertainment purposes, but this momentary implementation of real-life tragedy pales in comparison to the controversial approach of Bobby Pruitt's "Death Rituals."

Pruitt's extreme haunted attraction centers around three horror films whose narratives are, directly and indirectly, connected to bullying. But before customers even begin the haunt itself, they are treated to a number of real-life bullying cases that ended in tragedy. Wandering among the open areas of the warehouse where "Death Rituals" takes place are actors in "costume"—but not of monsters, zombies, or clowns. Instead, there are burn victims, men with gunshot wounds, and women with deformities and slashed wrists. One performer wears a noose around her neck, her shirt emblazoned with a photograph of a Canadian teenager who took her own life after years of being bullied.[2] An anti-bullying advocate and one of the few voices

---

[2] Amanda Todd committed suicide at the age of 15. Prior to her death, Todd had posted an online 9-minute video in which she used note cards to communicate her experiences with bullying, self-harm, and extortion.

to outright condemn extreme haunts, Bethany Treadwell has argued for a permanent closure of "Death Rituals," writing, "Gone are the days of glow-in-the-dark monsters and sheeted ghosts. Forget anything even remotely connected to the historical, familial, or celebratory aspects of Halloween. Pruitt's haunt is exploitation in its most raw form" (p. 3). Once participants enter the tunnel that begins the haunt proper, "Death Rituals" abandons reality in favor of fictional horror narratives that still serve to promote troubling themes.

Roger Spottiswoode's *Terror Train* opens with a scene of fraternity hazing gone wrong: a group of drunken med-students lures their unsuspecting friend into bed with a rotting female corpse stolen from the school's morgue. The experience drives the young man insane and leads to the vengeful tale of carnage that comprises the threadbare plot of the film. The first major set-piece of "Death Rituals" mimics this opening scene, as customers must climb into a bed with a "dead body." The actress playing the corpse is fully nude and slathered in stage blood, her face a rotting mask of skin erosions and open wounds. The "corpse" then springs to life, grabs the customers, and screams sexual vulgarities at them. When customers jump from the bed and attempt to escape into the next room, they are confronted by a gang of "frat brothers." In a modified parallel of *Terror Train*'s opening scene, the actors throw the customers onto the floor and wrap several layers of sheets around their heads. One male customer reported that the sheets were "soaked in something wet and rotten-smelling," while a female customer stated she could not see or breathe properly during the sequence. Another customer claimed the sheets were "drenched in urine" and other bodily fluids. Once the sheets are removed, customers are pushed up the stairs and corralled into the next level of the haunt.

Though Tobe Hooper's *The Texas Chain Saw Massacre* does not intentionally set out to address the theme of bullying, the movie's notorious dinner sequence includes scenes of physical violence and verbal humiliation against a young and helpless female victim. The vicious ways in which the members of the cannibal family—including one character who wears a mask made from human skin—mock and torment Sally Hardesty prefigure the bullying scenes of *Terror Train*, *Carrie*, and a host of other horror movies from the 1970s and 80s. Inside "Death Rituals," customers are tied to chairs made from animal bones and force-fed unidentified food from a bowl, all while being grabbed, prodded with sticks, and spit upon by actors dressed as characters from Hooper's film. In this same sequence, some customers have their eyelids pried open with speculums, while others, women especially, are forced to endure personal insults having to do with their gender and physical appearance. "My guests cry and scream and some actually puke all over themselves," Pruitt states. "And only then do they beg to be let out. They beg for their lovers. For their parents. They beg for everything and they get nothing." By the time participants are chased out of the room by a chainsaw-wielding giant, their clothes are shredded, their hair clumped with bacon grease, and their faces and bodies covered in fake blood, gobs of leftover food, and vomit.

The final set-piece of "Death Rituals" attempts to mirror the two most iconic scenes from Brian De Palma's *Carrie*. The movie, which tells the tragic story of a bullied girl's revenge on her malicious classmates, begins with a shower sequence inside a girls' locker room (for many, a place of ritualistic bullying). Here, the protagonist, 16-year-old Carrie White, has her period for the first time. Apparently unaware of menstruation, Carrie begins to panic, believing that she is bleeding to death. Disgusted but highly entertained by Carrie's terror and naïveté, her classmates begin to pelt Carrie with sanitary napkins and tampons. "Death Rituals" loosely follows this narrative as participants wander a maze-like set made up of rusted lockers and empty shower stalls. When participants turn a corner, they are attacked by a horde of women wearing homemade pig masks—a reference to the climax of the movie and a foreshadowing of the last set-piece of the haunt. From the showers, guests are chased onto a raised platform on the top floor of the warehouse. In the finale, the haunt's narrative captures the climactic prom sequence from *Carrie*, but without any indication of the protagonist's supernatural abilities. Amid falling streamers and balloons, participants have buckets of stage blood dumped on them from the rafters above. Inexplicably, the "pig girls" and "frat boys" return, shoving participants out an exit door and down a stairwell, ending the experience.

Ethical Issues and Real Violence in Extreme Haunts

Keager (2013) criticized some extreme haunted attractions for exploiting the sufferings of real people, especially victims who have been targets of vicious cruelty. Hendrickson (2013) argued that, despite the popularity of the true crime genre and horror films "based on actual events," it is often the families of the victims who must endure endless pain, refusing to accept that the death of their loved ones should be told as a "ghost story" or other form of entertainment. Williams (2013) questioned the hiring practices of certain extreme haunts, claiming that some "[extreme haunt] actors are underage or ex-convicts" (p. 10). Making a profit from real tragedy and using the likeness of people who have died to market haunted attractions are additional ethical issues within the industry. Although past literature has drawn attention to these concerns, evidence from personal interviews and "real time" observation may be the most effective way to expose the most disturbing truth of all about extreme haunts: some customers experience violence, sexual aggression, and psychological abuse when participating in them.

In the queue for Christopher Andersen's "The Underground," the recording of the story of Colleen Stan went largely unnoticed by the other customers, as most were either engaged in conversations or watching the crypt-keeper interact with the people about to enter the simulation. The recording itself lasts for two minutes and plays on a loop. It is performed much like a campfire tale or urban legend, replete with orchestral music and "haunted house" sound effects (including female screams and clanking chains). In post-haunt interviews, only a few of the customers could recall specific details from the story and none had actually ever heard of the Colleen Stan case. The woman's name is mentioned several times in the recording, but her image does not appear during the experience and her story is not a focal point of the haunt (C. Alvarez, observation, October 15, 2015). Justifying his use of true crime as part of a haunted house, Andersen says, "My objective when creating this haunt was to entertain and scare people, which can be problematic when real-life events come into play. I was careful to tell the [Colleen Stan] story as accurately as possible and without getting too graphic, and to treat her tragedy with respect." When asked why he failed to include the fact that Stan escaped from her abductors and that one of them was prosecuted for his crimes, Andersen stated, "That omission was strictly to heighten the intensity of the narrative—not to misconstrue the sad facts of the case." With Andersen's coarse but seemingly earnest attempt to present the Colleen Stan story in a new and creative medium, "The Underground" treads a thin line between entertainment and exploitation.

The BDSM-inspired appearance of the crypt-keeper, and his physical interaction with customers before they enter the coffin, are two further ethical concerns surrounding "The Underground." Of the interactions observed (several are noted earlier in this paper), the most alarming was of the woman who cried after the crypt-keeper grabbed her arm, shouted profanities at her, and insulted her physical appearance, which included sexually-charged remarks. The woman refused to enter the coffin, left the line, and demanded a refund from management (C. Alvarez, observation, October 15, 2015). While the flagrant misogyny and full-contact aggression were both troubling parts of the haunt, the psychology behind the character's behavior, says Andersen, prepares the customer for the actual burial simulation. "This isn't Disneyland. You're not supposed to feel safe or happy," he explains. "While we will continue to work on finding that balance between fear and genuine pain and embarrassment, we do intend for the burial to be the scariest thing the person has ever experienced. This is a haunt of the mind, and the crypt-keeper is the deranged sentinel of the casket." Later during the observation, customers were seen being shoved and taunted as they entered the coffin, but the actor's monologue was more akin to the scripted lines one might hear in a traditional haunted attraction. In response to this data, Andersen says,

"Every experience [with the haunt] is different, and we are learning from our mistakes and trying to create a terrifying and safe event that everyone can enjoy."

Unlike many extreme haunts, the pitch-darkness and hermetic space of "The Underground" are experienced alone, without the sudden appearance of lunging actors in costume. The coffin's timeworn façade and plush silk lining contribute to the haunt's macabre ambience, as do the sound effects (including the sounds of digging and slithering insects). Once a customer steps inside and lies down, the coffin is locked from the outside and provides no light or room to move. As pneumatic air cylinders jostle the coffin and mimic the feeling of being buried, the customer has no ability to escape before the experience is over unless he or she speaks the safe word. For these reasons, "The Underground" has been classified as extreme; however, the choice to use a safe word supports the ethicality of the haunt. "Because of the darkness and cramped space, people with anxiety disorders are discouraged from attempting the simulation," Andersen warns. "But not everyone listens to our advice and every year we have panic attacks. One time a girl peed inside the coffin! The safe word is there to prevent these kinds of problems." It should be noted that the majority of customers observed finished the haunt without using the safe word and had generally positive responses about the experience (C. Alvarez, observation, October 15, 2015). One man, a 23-year-old "haunted house veteran" who went through the burial simulator, said, "A haunted house doesn't need to assault you to be scary. It was a cool experience and I'd definitely do it again."

The ethical issues in Bobby Pruitt's "Death Rituals" are far more complex. Treadwell (2015) condemned the production for its "shameless exploitation" of real-life bullying victims (p. 4), while several of the participants were disgusted by the haunt's "cheap tactics" and "lack of empathy for people who have really suffered." While it is not difficult to argue against Pruitt's exploitation of real-life bullying and suicide victims, other aspects of the haunt are just as ethically corrupt. In the first set-piece that mimics the opening scene of *Terror Train*, the haunt features a naked woman, her face covered with open pink sores and erupted cysts, who traps "victims" in her bed and screams words of sexual violence. Marcus Spitzer, a member of Pruitt's production team, revealed that Pruitt hired his girlfriend, a dancer who goes by the stage moniker April Showers and suffers from severe cystic acne, to play the part, a decision that calls into question the ethicality of the haunt. It is not a character with make-up and prosthetics that becomes a source of abject horror and perverse sexuality, but rather the woman herself. In this way, Pruitt exploits real physical differences in an attempt to horrify and disgust his audience. The introduction of physical violence only makes the scene more contemptible. At the hands of the "frat boys," customers reported being pinched and grabbed. Women complained of having stage blood spit in their faces, strands of their hair chopped off with scissors, and being "felt up" by a character named "The Bully."[3] After telling the actors that a damp cloth had cut off her breathing, one woman was shoved to the floor and dragged around by her bare feet. Although Pruitt likens his haunt to "absurdist cinema" and argues that we live in a "society of violence and trauma," nothing can justify the human debasement at the core of his production. "Death Rituals" disguises assault and torture as cheap entertainment and fails in a way that is unethical and cruel.

In the next section of "Death Rituals," modeled after the dinner scene in *The Texas Chain Saw Massacre*, actors dressed as "hillbilly cannibals" use plastic zip-ties to bind and restrain the customers. Although the waiver states that participants may be "safely bound or gagged," two male customers said the zip-ties cut into their skin, causing welts or bleeding wounds. In this same sequence, customers are jabbed with sharp sticks, threatened with knives, and spit on. They are forced to eat from bowls of slop that participants identified as most likely dog food. "At first I thought it was spam, but it tasted metallic,

---

[3] Played by 35-year-old Colin Moore, who served five years in an Arizona state prison for felony domestic-violence stalking and domestic-violence burglary.

like chemical mush. I nearly threw up," a male participant said. In one instance, when a woman refused to eat the contents of her bowl, a character named "The Cannibal"[4] plucked live cockroaches from a jar and put them on the woman's face. "It was horrifying," the woman said. "They were real cockroaches, crawling all over me. They burrowed into my clothes. One of them got in my mouth. And when I got home, my face was covered in cockroach bites." Without question, the gross negligence and willful misrepresentation in "Death Rituals" undermine the haunt's ethicality. In addition to the violence and emotional anguish that customers endure, the lack of sterilization turns the haunt into a significant health risk, as customers are potentially exposed to illnesses transmitted through bodily fluids.[5] By Pruitt's own admission, "Death Rituals" offers no trained medical team on-site.

The final section of "Death Rituals," which borrows from the horror film *Carrie*, contains the haunt's most extreme form of bullying and sexual harassment. Though the film's iconic shower scene lays the groundwork for the satisfactory revenge sequence at the climax of the movie, the vile treatment of Carrie White rarely becomes physical. However, in "Death Rituals," after customers wander a maze of gym lockers and shower stalls, they are confronted by a group of screaming women wearing pig masks. As described by one female participant: "At least two of them were naked from the waist down. No underwear on or anything. And they had blood between their legs and smeared over their thighs. They spun me and my friend around, making us dizzy, and then one of the naked ones grinded on us and shoved wet tampons in our mouths before chasing us out." Unlike other haunted house

---

[4] Played by 46-year-old Clive Langer, a bodybuilder and ex-convict who served 10 years in Kern Valley State Prison in California for involuntary manslaughter.
[5] Not to mention the fact that cockroaches contaminate everything they touch, passively transporting infectious pathogens that are potentially dangerous to humans.

attractions that have vowed to never portray scenes of sexual violence or aberrant sexual activity, "Death Rituals" revels in psychosexual degradation and abuse. In the final scene of the haunt, customers are pushed onto a platform on the top floor of the warehouse, where buckets of stage blood are dropped onto them from above. Prom music and falling streamers signal the return of the "pig girls" and "frat boys," who bring the haunt to a vile conclusion. One male participant described being forced out the exit door by the half-naked women, which left his female friend alone with three or four male actors. "They circled me. They called me fat and pinched my belly. They laughed at me. They told me I was too ugly to fuck, so they would just have to kill me instead," the female said. "One of the guys flipped me around and threw me against the wall. This other one grabbed my hips from behind and bent me over. Then he forced something wet and gooey between my legs—I don't know exactly what it was." Several other participants in the haunt, most of them female, complained of similar issues and stated that they were emotionally distressed by the experience of going through the haunt. This disturbing attempt to take the haunted house concept into new territory has crossed an ethical line, but as Sanders (2015) explained, "Pruitt's waiver provides the legal loophole that he and his mentally-disturbed actors need in order to freely torture and sexually assault young women" (p. 24).

Conclusion

This paper has examined both the interpretation and narrative approach of two extreme haunted houses in California. Through personal interviews and observations, it has also explored the role that ethics play when constructing extreme haunted houses and the ways in which a lack of ethics can negatively impact those who participate in such experiences. Although Andersen and Pruitt argue that their objective is to provide seasonal entertainment while turning a profit, there is little doubt that the controversy over such haunted attractions comes primarily from serious ethical and narrative concerns having to do with real violence, sexual aggression, and other forms of abuse. This study has also demonstrated that extreme haunted houses, especially those like "Death Rituals," should be approached with great caution by customers. While many producers in the haunt industry are attempting to entertain without exploiting real victims of violent crime, others are committing legal torture and reducing human suffering to a commodity.

"College Paper Causes Halloween Horror Showdown" by George Matthews (originally published in *The National Dish*, January, 2016, p. 4-7):

A research paper about the violent mistreatment of visitors to a haunted attraction in Southern California has sparked a spirited debate among horror fanatics and feminists alike.

Cherie Alvarez, an 18-year-old college student from the San Francisco Bay Area and the author of the paper, has exposed the terrifying truth behind "Death Rituals," a raunchy haunted house that entertained and disgusted visitors in October of last year.

Interviewing several men and women who entered the haunted attraction only to be verbally and physically abused, Alvarez has denounced a growing industry that is no longer content with delivering the illusion of horror.

The paper's anonymous quotes reveal that customers of "Death Rituals" were punched, kicked, and forced to ingest toxic substances, all in the name of sleazy Halloween entertainment.

The paper, which Alvarez sent to magazines and websites about the haunt industry, features graphic details that police might view as physical and sexual assault.

According to official sources, Alvarez and two of her friends also went through the gross-out haunted house and experienced their own share of unruly treatment, including bullying and sexual harassment.

The media attention has generated protests against the producer of the sick attraction, 37-year-old Bobby Pruitt, who is currently developing a new project that promises to be even more twisted than the last. Online petitions are now calling for a mass boycott of Pruitt's future events.

The National Dish has made a number of alarming discoveries about Pruitt, a man so depraved that he hired criminals to run his attraction and forced his girlfriend, topless dancer Tiffany Cobb (otherwise known as "April Showers"), 36, to perform inside the haunt.

In an even more stunning revelation, our crack cyber-investigators have uncovered television transcripts that reveal Bobby Pruitt's past troubles with the law.

The transcripts detail unsettling truths about Pruitt's young life, including a knife attack that he committed against one of his mother's female friends, his time spent in a juvenile detention facility, and a home environment distinguished by alcohol, drug use, and kinky sex.

The lead investigator who stumbled upon Pruitt's troubled past commented, "Pruitt was a juvenile at the time, so a forgiving judge scrubbed his record of any old charges. But Pruitt's family had agreed to participate in a TV show about his story. The show never aired, but we managed to get hold of the transcript. And that's where we found a treasure chest of disturbing intelligence on this guy and his girlfriend."

According to *The National Dish*'s inside source, Tiffany Cobb is a struggling alcoholic who ekes out a living by dancing in skid-row strip clubs and performing in pornographic stage shows.

Lynn Chelton, an Ohio-based advocate for teenagers, felt suspicious of Pruitt the first moment that she learned about "Death Rituals." Chelton created several online petitions on social media sites after reading about the attraction, its strange owner and criminal performers, and the traumatic experiences customers have had inside.

"Anyone visiting these attractions need to understand that the waiver you sign doesn't protect you from real physical and psychological abuse," she told media outlets. "I don't want to turn on the news one day and hear that someone has died at one of these things."

"Death Rituals" took place in a Los Angeles warehouse that Pruitt had populated with a number of grotesque characters, including real-life suicide and gunshot victims. The haunted house also took its inspiration from Hollywood's most notorious horror movies, including *Carrie*, a sordid tale about a psychotic teenager who murders her classmates in cold blood.

Mark D'Angelo, the executive producer of an extreme haunted house called "Execution," has said that he stands against the premise of "Death Rituals" and vowed to make changes to his own Halloween events to protect the safety of his customers.

"I've met Cherie and other women who have had these awful experiences, and it's not something I want to be a part of," D'Angelo explained to a Los Angeles news agency.

In the horror rags and blogs willing to interview him, Pruitt has defended his product from arguments like D'Angelo's by saying that he "finds poetry and trash indistinguishable" and believes "the composition of ugliness in [his] work is at once physical, spiritual, and emotional."

When asked about the research paper that denounces his work, Pruitt told a magazine called *Haunted America*, "No one tells lies about me and gets away with it."

Adding fuel to this raging fire, *The National Dish* has learned from an exclusive source that Tiffany Cobb, who attacked people inside the haunt, has received death threats through social media outlets like Twitter and Facebook.

According to the source, a clandestine movement is now underway to stop Pruitt's next haunted attraction before it gets off the ground.

Despite these obstacles, Pruitt has insisted that his next project will surpass the realistic horrors of "Death Rituals" and that he intends to hold the event at a time other than Halloween to keep the interest low-key and underground. This new haunt has been rumored to take place almost entirely outdoors and to involve surveillance and abduction scenarios.

"I may be a worm in the apple," Pruitt was quoted as saying, "but you don't touch my girl or my team. You don't come after us. We come after *you*. We decide who has the power."

Although Pruitt and Cobb have been targeted by angry customers and protest groups, he's not the only one participating in this disturbing game of shock entertainment. Many other haunted attractions have used real events and violent situations as the basis for their storylines and characters.

Lance Berryman, a reporter for *Haunters Monthly* magazine, has cited haunted attractions like "The World of Horrors" and "The Devil's Business: Manson's House of Blood," which was based on the infamous Tate/LaBianca murders of 1969, as examples. "Death Rituals," Berryman argued, is "surreal participatory art" and is not nearly as violent as its critics claim.

"Movies have been using real tragedy as the basis for their plots for decades, and people protested those, too," he said. "Once the furor dies down, Bobby Pruitt will be recognized for what he is: a mad visionary who produces creative and deeply philosophical work."

From "Catch and Release: The Shocking Truth Behind the Juvenile Justice System" (unaired episode of KICU-TV's *Hardline News*, printed here with permission from Cox Media Group):

THIS IS A RUSH TRANSCRIPT OF AN UNAIRED EPISODE. COURTROOM FOOTAGE HAS BEEN NOTED APPROPRIATELY. ALL OTHER INTERVIEWS WERE RECORDED AS PART OF AN INTENDED BROADCAST.

Produced and Directed by Mary Carol DuBois
Written by Sampson Cole and Mary Carol DuBois

CHRISTOPHER VINSON, Announcer: Bobby Pruitt became a peeping tom at the age of 12, stalking his quiet Ohio town in the dead of night and peering into the windows of his neighbors. Soon after, he began getting into fights at school. A withdrawn boy, he developed an interest in the macabre works of Dean Koontz and Stephen King, and he immersed himself in the goriest horror movies he could find— movies with titles like *Faces of Death* and *Bloodsucking Freaks*. In his freshman year of high school Bobby began to write and to draw, and his life seemed to take new direction when he found a girlfriend—a 15-year-old, blue-eyed blonde named Tiffany. Bobby and Tiffany shared a passion for the arts, and Bobby began working for haunted attractions and other Halloween events in his hometown. Then, at the age of 16, Bobby unexpectedly and brutally attacked his mother's girlfriend, stabbing the defenseless woman with a paint scraper and nearly killing her.

Tonight, in an exclusive report, *Hardline News* correspondent Sampson Cole investigates this controversial story and raises important questions about the state of our juvenile justice system.

SAMPSON COLE, Correspondent: Today, stories of crime and violence dominate our airwaves. Every moment we are learning of some new tragedy—a husband kills his wife in cold blood; a man invades a home and commits a savage murder; a kidnapping results in the death of a child. But what if I told you that there exists an even darker undercurrent to our country's crime problem? What if I told you that some of the most violent acts today are committed by kids under the age of 18? It's true—and the communities impacted by these crimes are fed up. They believe that violent children, especially repeat offenders, deserve to be prosecuted to the full extent of the law—perhaps even to be prosecuted as adults and sentenced to lengthy prison terms.

DANIEL STROMBERG, Public Defender: (courtroom footage) Your Honor, Robert Nathaniel Pruitt is a 16-year-old boy charged with attempted murder.

COLE: Typically, juvenile courts are closed to the public, but the superior court of Washington County has granted the footage and interviews in this exclusive report. Through the story of a polarizing young man who committed an act of stunning violence, *Hardline News* brings you a rare glimpse into a private world—the world of the juvenile justice system.

(OVER PHOTOGRAPHS OF BOBBY PRUITT)

COLE: Here is 16-year-old Robert Pruitt, a resident of a quiet suburb in Marietta, Ohio. Bobby is wearing a denim jacket, and on the right shoulder is an iron-on patch from the 1931 film version of *Dracula*, one of his favorite movies. Bobby is charged with attempted murder. The victim is his mother's partner, Roxanne Johnson.

ROXANNE JOHNSON: (courtroom footage) Your Honor, as you know, my name's Roxanne Johnson, and Bobby, this boy sitting here, is my girlfriend's son. I've known Bobby his whole life—ever since he was born. And I'm standing in this courtroom today because of an altercation between us on the night of October 15th, 1994. That night, after a party at the house, Bobby picked up a scraper knife and attacked me with it.

COLE: (voiceover) It happened in October, with heavy rains falling outside and the Pruitt household in disarray after a late-night party.

CHARITY PRUITT, Bobby's mother: We had thrown a party with some of our friends. One of them, a guy I didn't know very well, a militant-type, started reading some poetry, really heavy stuff, and things got crazy. People were boozing, drinking rum, getting into fights. After everyone left I fell asleep on the couch. I woke up later to this awful screaming inside the house. Someone was shouting, "Stop! Please stop!" I didn't know it at the time, but it was Roxanne begging for her life.

ROXANNE: I was standing in the kitchen, a glass of wine in my hand, with my back to the hallway. All the lights were off. Then suddenly someone was on my back, clawing my neck. The wine glass shattered on the floor. I tried swinging him off me, but I wasn't strong enough. Then I smelled the cherry pop on his breath. That's how I knew it was Charity's boy. Bobby loves cherry pop.

COLE: You must have been terrified.

ROXANNE: All I knew was I had to get him off. At first I thought he was trying to choke me, but then I felt something wet and sticky on my hands. It was my own blood pouring out of me.

COLE: (voice-over) Using a paint scraper he found in the garage, Bobby was stabbing his mother's partner repeatedly in the back, neck, and on the sides of her face.

STROMBERG: Bobby lacerated Ms. Johnson's right ear, splitting the lobe in half. He dug the blade of the scraper into the back shoulders. He severed the tendons in Ms. Johnson's hands. He jabbed the scraper into Ms. Johnson's right eye and her throat.

ROXANNE: Somehow I got Bobby on the floor. The scraper slid under the kitchen table. Bobby crumpled up, out of breath, his hands covered in my blood. He had blood smeared across his face and hair. And then he crawled under the table and grabbed the scraper. I braced myself. I thought he was going to come at me again, but he began stabbing himself in the neck. He didn't go deep, but he has a scar there now—about three inches—right across the throat.

COLE: Police and medical help arrived minutes after Charity's terrified call to 911. While officers collected evidence from the home, a pair of ambulances drove the wounded to the nearest hospital.

CHARITY: I saw Bobby first thing that morning. He was in his hospital bed, his skin pale as death. His eyes were glassy, like he was drugged. He had a bandage on his neck. I hugged him a long while. And then I asked him, "Bobby, why did you do this horrible thing?" And that was when he started to cry. He said, "Mom, I don't remember doing anything wrong. Mom, what did I do?"

COLE: Bobby, at what point did you realize you had done something terrible?

BOBBY: A cop came to take my statement in the hospital, and I asked him, "Statement for what?" And he gave me this cold stare and told me things would go a lot easier for me if I just told the truth. He asked me if I used drugs. He said, "You stabbed your mother's friend. You stabbed a woman. Don't act like you don't know what I'm talking about." I told him he was crazy. I told him I didn't remember. He said, "Kid, right now we got you for attempted murder. But if the woman dies, we'll get you for first-degree manslaughter."

COLE: If you couldn't remember what had happened, how did you interpret what the officer was saying to you?

BOBBY: It was like a nightmare come to life, man. I thought maybe someone had slipped me some bad dope.

COLE: On the night of the attack, Bobby had smoked marijuana with Tiffany and they both swallowed a form of amphetamine called a "benny"—a pill that stimulates the central nervous system. Among his friends at school, Bobby was known as a regular drug user, which resulted in his only brush with the law prior to the attack on Roxanne Johnson. In 1992, in order to buy drugs, Bobby had stolen money from another kid at school. Bobby was charged in juvenile court with strong-arm robbery and was sentenced to probation for 6 months.

DOMINICO ZAPPULA, Probation Officer: You have to do more than read the case file. You have to talk to the kid. Look into his eyes.

You have to dig beneath the surface to find out what's really going on with him.

COLE: Bobby's probation officer learned that the small, split-level home where the Pruitts lived was hiding its share of dark secrets. At the age of 14, Bobby was doing more than getting into fights at school. He was smoking pot and taking illegal pills. He wrote disturbing poetry and filled notebooks with sketches of movie monsters and pornographic drawings. He and Tiffany were experimenting sexually and reading books about cults and witchcraft. And he wasn't the only one in the house with a substance abuse problem. His mother was an alcoholic.

ZAPPULA: Charity Pruitt threw wild parties. Loud music, lots of drinking and drug use. Bobby would bring Tiffany to the house, and they would smoke weed and drink vodka in one room while his mother and Roxanne and their friends partied in another room. But Bobby and his mother remained close. When I first met Bobby, my first thought was, "Here's a kid who would do anything for his mom."

ROXANNE: When news of the attack first came out, people assumed I was doing something to hurt Charity. That Bobby was protecting her from me. But that's not true. Charity and I have known each other since junior high. I love her, and I treated Bobby like he was my own flesh and blood.

CHARITY: One afternoon, when Bobby was around 11-years-old, he walked in on me and Roxanne kissing. From that point on, he had a hard time accepting that I was in love with another woman.

COLE: Today, Bobby is facing the possibility of being tried in adult court. If convicted of attempted murder there, the 16-year-old faces a mandatory sentence of 15 years to life. A staunch defender of her son, Charity Pruitt remains fearful that her only child will spend the next several years in a state prison. But much to everyone's surprise, the prosecutors in the case offer a deal—if Bobby will plead guilty, he can remain in juvenile court.

CHARITY: It was too risky not to keep Bobby in juvenile court. I begged him to plead guilty to the charge. I told him I would stay by his side. We really had no choice.

TIFFANY COBB, Bobby's girlfriend: As tough as Bobby was, a lot of it was acting. Things he had learned from books and Charles Bronson movies. But I knew how gentle he could be. I thought that, if he went prison, he probably would die there.

COLE: Trusting the input of his mother, his girlfriend, and his defense attorney, Bobby decides to take the deal. Judge Franklin Moseley will hear the case. In an attempt to determine the motive behind the attack on Ms. Johnson, Judge Moseley orders an independent psychological evaluation of Bobby Pruitt—and the psychologist returns with an unexpected report. She argues that Bobby suffers from intermittent explosive disorder, a behavioral disorder characterized by sudden outbursts of anger and violence, often to the point of uncontrollable rage. As a result of the report, Bobby's lawyer prepares a new argument in his defense: Bobby did not have the physical or emotional ability to control his impulses when he attacked Roxanne Johnson.

DR. MARIA HUERTA, Behavioral Psychologist: Intermittent explosive disorder outbursts are unpremeditated and impulsive. They involve aggressive behavior disproportionate to the source triggers. So while Bobby may have felt angry or confused about his mother's close relationship with Ms. Johnson, the knife attack was in no way planned. Also, people with IED often become victims of substance abuse. Bobby was a known drug user. We know he smoked marijuana that night and that he has no concrete memory of the stabbing. However, now that he has been informed of the attack and even seen photographic evidence of his actions, Bobby has shown genuine remorse. These are all symptoms of someone with IED.

COLE: Although prosecutors keep up their end of the bargain— Bobby has remained in the juvenile system—his family is still deeply concerned about his mental health and safety. The defense wants Bobby to receive immediate substance abuse counseling. They want him to see a therapist. But the prosecution wants the troubled teenager sent to Ohio's toughest facility for juveniles: the Clermont County Juvenile Detention Center.

STROMBERG: (courtroom footage) Clermont County cannot be an option for Bobby. The Pruitt family has unresolved conflicts among them, none of which will be solved by a detention center historically known for incidents of violence and abuse. Bobby has a serious disorder. He and his mother have a problem with drugs and alcohol. Bobby's girlfriend, Tiffany, has also admitted to a dependency on alcohol. They are all bonded in very unhealthy ways. But if they can get sober, the violence in the home and their reliance on dangerous substances will end.

PIERCE: (courtroom footage) Mr. Stromberg has very idyllic notions about the future of this family, but his argument conveniently overlooks the facts of the case. Bobby Pruitt tried to kill another human being—a defenseless woman—a long-time member of the family. For such a callous and cowardly act, Clermont County is the only alternative.

COLE: (voice-over) After taking a week to deliberate the case, Judge Moseley reaches a decision.

JUDGE FRANKLIN MOSELEY: (courtroom footage) In this case, the court must assure a successful rehabilitation for the defendant, and it must also take measure to prevent any Pruitt family member or some third party from becoming a victim to Bobby's violent impulses. In order to reach these expectations, the court has determined that Bobby Pruitt will spend the next 90 days at the Clermont County Juvenile Detention Center, where he will be observed until the court can make a final ruling about the circumstances that have brought us here today.

COLE: And so the wait continues. As Bobby undergoes his 90-day evaluation at Clermont County, his mother remains frightened about what might happen to her son behind those towering walls of brick and steel.

CHARITY: As a child Bobby stuck close to my side. He'd get afraid when I had friends over. Roxanne and I would be listening to music, or making supper, and Bobby would hide behind the couch. But now that he's older, he's discovered art and poetry and books. He loses himself in movies and plays. During all my visits to the courthouse, I've seen some of the other juveniles in the system. They're scary-looking boys. They're not poets. They're not artists. Bobby will be a target at Clermont County. That place is nothing more than a breeding ground for hardcore criminals.

BOBBY: I'm afraid to go to Clermont. For the first time in my life, I'm really afraid I'm going to die. That judge made a mistake. I mean, look at me. Just how long do you think I can survive in a hole like that?

TIFFANY: I wrote him a letter every day he was gone. I told him I loved him and missed him. I got this tattoo on my wrist, this little oak leaf here, to symbolize the cycle of life and our journey together. But I couldn't pay attention in school without Bobby around. My grades got bad. I was taking photography and trying to build a portfolio, but the teacher said my pictures weren't any good. He said I was holding the camera wrong.

COLE: During the bus ride to the detention center in Clermont County, Bobby does his best to put up a brave front.

(ON BUS RIDE)

BOBBY: I've been here before. I came up here for strong-arm robbery, but they could only keep me for 11 days before they had to cut me loose. Now they nail me on an attempted murder charge. The prosecution wanted to throw me in adult court and hang me up. I was like, "Fuck it, I'm guilty. You wouldn't send a guilty kid to prison, would you?"

COLE: How has hard time changed you, Bobby?

BOBBY: At Clermont I had to pretend to be somebody else. Like, I couldn't have any of my books around. For a while I kept a journal of my drawings under my bunk, and all of Tiffany's letters and poems, but I had to throw them away. I couldn't risk getting caught with that shit. And I never told Tiffany. I lied and said the guards took her letters and tossed them.

COLE: Bobby has now returned to juvenile hall from Clermont. His evaluation there went poorly. Within just a few days of his arrival, Bobby got into serious trouble.

BOBBY: They put me in a room with a 17-year-old rapist. A religious quack—always spouting off Bible verses and talking about the blood of the lamb. Telling me I had to get saved. Everyone was a sinner, everyone was evil and filthy and perverted, except for little kids—they were the holy ones, he said, the ones that Jesus chose to serve in His name. He slept with his Bible—kept it right under his pillow. I tried to ignore him and go about my business. A few days later, I'm out with gen pop for the first time. And things went bad from there.

COLE: During a pick-up basketball game, Bobby says, an older kid walked up to him, showed him a knife, and told Bobby he had to make a choice.

BOBBY: The knife was made out of a toothbrush and razor blades. The kid was like, "Your roommate's a rapist. You gotta rape him or kill him." The kid grabbed me by my shirt and pressed the knife against my cheek. He nicked me. He said, "This ain't juvie. This is Clermont. What you gonna do?"

COLE: That same afternoon, a guard was monitoring the corridors in Bobby's wing. The guard caught Bobby holding the knife to the side of his roommate's head while attempting to sodomize him. According to the guard, Bobby had stuffed pages torn from the Bible into his roommate's mouth so that no one would hear his cries for help.

COLE: (to Bobby) How do you feel about what you did to your roommate?

BOBBY: I didn't have a choice. I wasn't going to kill him, but I couldn't go back to the yard and face those other guys. I'd be dead. I'd get punked for whatever dignity I had left, and then I'd be dead. He didn't mean anything to me—he was just another con. But you make enemies every day in a place like that. It didn't matter.

COLE: (to Stromberg) Shortly after his arrival at Clermont County, Bobby commits a sexual assault against his roommate. He uses a knife and threatens to cut the boy's throat if he doesn't comply. Bobby has pled guilty to the charges. Does all of this change your angle on his case?

STROMBERG: No. I was surprised by what happened at Clermont, but Bobby wouldn't have been there in the first place if he had received the proper treatment.

COLE: But consider his record. Can you really blame all of these acts on intermittent explosive disorder? At what point does the court say, "This is a dangerous kid who needs to be locked up?"

STROMBERG: He's mentally ill. He has extreme overreactions to certain events and thinks to solve them only through intimidation and violence. He has problems with women. He might be suicidal. In terms of his health and the safety of others, he's better off getting some serious counseling and medication.

COLE: More than eight months have passed since Bobby attacked his mother's girlfriend. Judge Moseley is ready to sentence Bobby for the attempted murder. But the stakes are even more serious now, as Bobby must contend with the sexual offense.

JUDGE MOSELEY: (courtroom footage) Since we last met, we have new reports to consider, plus the evaluation submitted by the CCJDC. The focus of the court today is on you, Bobby. What do you have to say?

BOBBY: (reading in the courtroom) Your Honor, three days after I got to Clermont County, I was approached by another boy with a shiv. He nicked me with it—right here, on my cheek. This boy gave me an ultimatum. With all my heart I believed that if I did not do what this boy was asking, I was going to be killed. I do not want to die, Your Honor. That is why I did what I did. I'm not a rapist. I'm not a sexual predator. I'm just a 17-year-old kid who wants to live a productive life. Your Honor, my evaluation from Clermont County is not a true judge of my character. The boy being judged in those reports is not me, but he is the boy that I will become if I am forced to spend the next several years in prison. Your Honor, I am hoping you became a judge to help people. I am here today asking for that help—not only for me, but also for my family and for my girlfriend. Please give us the help we need.

JUDGE MOSELEY: (courtroom footage) Thank you, Bobby. I'd like to give your mother the opportunity to speak on your behalf.

CHARITY: (reading in the courtroom) Your Honor, they locked my son up with a rapist, a person who uses religion as an excuse for his immoral behavior. He would have killed my son if given the chance, and he would have said God told him to do it. That's why the other inmates told Bobby to hurt this boy, Your Honor. They were afraid. They manipulated Bobby. They tricked him into doing this terrible thing. And if Bobby is forced to return to Clermont, that boy will mark him for death. I'm begging you—please don't let that happen to my son.

COLE: The prosecution responds with fiery determination.

PIERCE: (courtroom footage) Your Honor, I urge the court to take into deep consideration what the defendant and his loved ones are suggesting. The defendant and his supporters seem to feel justified in acting out violently on impulses. Imagine the next person to come face to face with Bobby Pruitt's uncontrollable rage—imagine what will become of that person. For the safety of the general public, this defendant needs to be kept away from decent society.

COLE: Judge Moseley begins by addressing the sexual offense.

JUDGE MOSELEY: (courtroom footage) While the violation of Penal Code 288 at the juvenile detention center was clearly an egregious assault, the court is not in the position to disregard the circumstances that led to the incident. Bobby's argument is that it was a one-time occurrence brought about by factors beyond his control. And the court agrees with that assessment.

COLE: Judge Moseley goes on to address the attack on Roxanne Johnson.

JUDGE MOSELEY: (courtroom footage) The court acknowledges that Bobby suffers from intermittent explosive disorder, which can lead to impulsive decision-making and inexplicable acts of rage. More to the point, the attack on Ms. Johnson, while certainly not excusable by any means, was the result of a serious behavioral condition and not a genuine desire to hurt an innocent woman. The court believes that the solution to Bobby's problems lies within the bonds of his family and his relationship with Tiffany Cobb. We need to restore those bonds in a healthy way. Therefore, Bobby will remain in Washington County juvenile hall until he turns 19. Clermont County will remain a possibility if Bobby displays any violent behavior. In this way, our community will stay safe while this young man and his family and loved ones get the help they so desperately need.

PIERCE: Frankly, I was stunned. What kind of message does the judge's ruling send out to the rest of society? Most of the young men who pass through juvenile court have had a rough life. Why does Bobby Pruitt deserve special treatment?

COLE: Even the public defender seems surprised by Judge Moseley's decision.

STROMBERG: Bobby caught a break. It's sad to say, but there are far worse cases and more deeply troubled kids out there. Whether fair or not, the court has to pick its battles.

COLE: In addition to allowing Bobby to serve his time in Washington County's juvenile hall, Judge Moseley gives him permission to leave during the day for counseling sessions and drug rehabilitation.

CHARITY: I'm hoping he'll graduate high school and start taking college classes. He's expressed interest in performing and set design. He wants to get a job and earn a living.

TIFFANY: If we can both get clean and sober, we want to start working on creative projects together. I want to be a professional photographer. I want to move to Hollywood and take pictures of all the big stars. And I want Bobby with me forever.

PIERCE: I'll remember Bobby Pruitt's name for a long time. It's a name I associate with darkness and anger. I just hope I don't open up the paper one day and see that he has reoffended and taken the life of an innocent person.

BOBBY: When I was at Clermont, I found this psychology book in the library. It said every human being has a dark side. Everyone has aggression and the drive to be violent. Some are just better at hiding it than others. I don't want to end up in jail again. I don't want to spend my life in prison. If I ever experience that kind of rage again, I'll have to bottle it up. Or find some kind of artistic outlet. In the future, I want people to think of me and smile. I want them to see me as a normal person, even if on the inside I'm falling apart.

"Horror Homage: The Inspiration Behind 'Personal Demons'" by Bobby Pruitt (originally published on *Lance Berryman's Pure Terror Blog*, February, 2016):

Wes Craven's *The Hills Have Eyes* (1977) tells the brutal story of two warring families—one "civilized" and the other "wild"—in a gruesome fight for survival. The movie pits "Big Bob" Carter and his wife and children against cannibal mutants with a thirst for blood. Throughout the film, the orange-hued landscape of the Nevada Desert ripples with blinding heat, while the jagged rocks and caves provide camouflage for Papa Jupiter and his gang of savages. But at night the desert turns black, enabling the killers to stalk and terrorize the Carters with ease. The savages kidnap Bob Carter, crucify him on a tree, and set him on fire; a deformed cannibal scavenges the family trailer for meat and milk; and in the film's most graphic sequence, another cannibal drinks blood from the severed head of a bird and rapes Brenda, one of the Carter daughters. Far from the comforts of home, surrounded by a vast desert, the Carters are rendered helpless. They roam the dark like hunted animals, their weapons and technology useless against the hungry desert rats. Only when the Carters learn how to become savages themselves do they begin to win the war against the cannibals—a reminder that we are all pitiless killing machines at heart.

"Personal Demons," a dusk-to-dawn horror simulation, will take guests on a journey through a blistering environment not dissimilar to the one Craven presents in his iconic masterpiece. Taking place in an undisclosed outdoor location in the Indio Desert, this overnight camping experience casts you in the role of an unsuspecting traveler forced to confront an evil that surpasses the scope of human understanding. Like the Carter family, participants will have few supplies at their disposal—a tent, a lighted compass, a tin of food, a crude map—but little else. They will be left alone in unfamiliar terrain and made to hunt a vicious tribe that is always watching—from the hills, from the pillars of craggy rock, and from the sand dunes high above the desert floor. The only way to survive the night is to strategize, scavenge for needed items, and defeat the monsters that crave your sex and hunger for your death.

Welcome to "Personal Demons"—a haunted attraction where ancient mythologies awaken, and where your worst fears about society and about yourself are realized.

Disclaimer: During "Personal Demons" you will be subjected to acts of violence and torture that straddle the line between simulation and real-life pain and terror. You will become a victim to the elements, including rapidly changing temperatures and rough terrain. The mature content of "Personal Demons" is unsuitable for anyone under the age of 21. Tickets will be limited and based on availability.

COMMENTS:

Catlover2001
2 hours ago

The owner will be sued after this event becomes "the disaster in the desert." There's way too much unpredictability here for this "simulation" to turn out well. I hope Pruitt has his attorneys at the ready. And his checkbook.

TikiTerror
2 hours ago

I attended this guy's previous haunt, "Death Rituals," and it was seriously fucked up. One of the actors, this big dude with a melon head and breath that smelled like fish, smacked me in the face and tried to grab my tits. I hit him back and got kicked out. That's the problem with these new "extreme" haunts. Customers aren't going to put up with this crap anymore. They want to be scared, not terrorized, and they'll fight back if they have to.

Texanchainsaw18
1 hour ago

Hell yeah. Sounds like the horror version of "Survivor," but with mutant hillbillies and psychopaths. Sign me up.

ClaireM.
1 hour ago

I agree with TikiTerror. Someone's going to get seriously hurt or even killed at one of these things. Notice the article doesn't say anything about trained medical staff onsite. It doesn't recommend what clothes guests should wear in the desert at night. What about water? A "tin" of food? Transportation? This doesn't sound safe at all.

JumpingJack
1 hour ago

I'm definitely going to this, but if one of these inbred monsters tries to grab my junk, I'll fuck his shit up.

Scary-chick
45 min ago

It's not like they're just going to let you beat on them without defending themselves, JumpingJack. You better be careful.

JumpingJack
40 min ago

I'd like to see 'em try, Scary-chick. I doubt they're going to frisk us for weapons before entering. And don't worry—I have a special little knife for occasions just like this.

Animalplanet
35 min ago

Two important questions: what types of people agree to work in these haunts? And who willingly pays money to go through them?

KingJames
20 min ago

"Fear him who can destroy both soul and body in hell." —Matthew 10:28. I'm coming for you, Mr. Pruitt. And we'll see then just how willing you are to embrace the beauty of death.

Jennifear
10 min ago

I went to "Death Rituals" because I dig horror movies and wanted the adrenaline rush. My group read the waiver and knew it was going to be rough. But about 20 minutes into the haunt, this creepy little pipsqueak with ginger hair put his hand down the back of my shorts. He basically tried to finger my ass. I turned around and scratched his face with my keys. They threw me out but I managed to get my money back from the nice girl running the ticket booth. I understand about touching, getting tied up, and other simulated acts. But this was real-life assault. My advice to anyone going to these types of haunted attractions is to bring something to protect yourself. Keys, pepper spray, a finger kubaton...even a small bottle opener or penknife on your keychain will work.

Nonya Bidnezz
7 min ago

Bobby Pruitt spins a horrific yarn, and I admire his tenacity after his last public relations disaster, but this sounds unnecessarily dangerous. For one thing, it's going to be freezing in the desert at night. The weather, combined with the war-like atmosphere of the simulation, is going to piss everyone off. I'm not sure who to be more afraid of—the actors or the people attending.

Countryboy
Just now

What the hell is a finger kubaton?

"Ticket to Hell: Married Couple Sues Haunted House Company" by Sparkle Donahue (originally published in *Desert Star Chatter*, March, 2016, p. 2-3):

A married couple has filed a lawsuit after an outdoor "horror simulation" forced them into bondage, captivity, and other extreme situations.

In the freezing-cold desert where the event took place, Tom and Jennifer Hansen, both age 26, lasted two hours before they fled the grounds and called police. They claimed to have suffered severe physical and emotional distress and reported to law enforcement a narrative of depravity and calculated violence.

A naked woman vomiting blood onto guests. A man biting the head off a live canary. Tomahawks, cattle prods, and rusty fish hooks used in all sorts of disgusting ways.

These graphic details and more haunt the pages of the lengthy written statement the Hansens provided to police.

Now they are suing the company's owner, Bobby Pruitt, a 38-year-old horror "aesthete" who designs haunted attractions that push legal boundaries by requiring guests to engage in acts of brutality and other deviant behavior.

The Hansens want their $100 ticket fee returned to them, but they are also seeking unspecified damages for their mental trauma and suffering.

The couple bought tickets to the simulation and attended the event on last Saturday evening, unaware of the vile horrors that would soon befall them like victims in a slasher flick.

Before the simulation began, the Hansens were given a flashlight, a pencil-sketched map of the area, a bag of nuts and other dried foods, and a canteen of water. As darkness descended, they were instructed to explore the desert in search of items needed to survive a night in the desolate terrain.

But the Hansens had barely started their adventure when a group of actors, dressed as flesh-starved cannibals and kill-crazy mutants, began tracking their movements from the tall rocks and sand dunes nearby.

"Right from the beginning, nothing felt right," Tom said, his face ashen and his hands trembling. "This wasn't a game to them. I took drama classes in college and I understand method acting—but this was *real* terror and *real* psychotic behavior."

Attacked by the performers in the haunt, the couple had their clothes cut open with shears, their faces smeared with stage blood and other foreign substances, and their lives threatened in ways that Jennifer described as "perverted and sadistic."

"And these people had the means to carry out their threats," Jennifer insisted. "They had weapons at their disposal, and they put us in positions where we had no choice but to fight back."

During one scuffle, an actress dressed in gore-soaked rags tried to fondle Jennifer's breasts and paint her exposed midriff with "witchy" symbols, but Jennifer resisted and ran off with her husband. The pair was forced to separate when Tom was tied up with strips of rawhide and dragged away by a man he described as "wet and slippery with blood."

The husband and wife quickly discovered that this overnight camping experience, which they believed was meant to replicate a "scary scavenger hunt," was a sick experiment gone terribly wrong.

Bone-cold weather conditions, human monsters who dished out vile sexual epithets, and a half-naked, tattooed woman with a serrated knife tormented the couple, who said they are among many guests of the event who are outraged by the experience.

The simulation, titled "Personal Demons," is inspired by the 1977 horror film *The Hills Have Eyes*, which tells the gruesome story of an innocent family's fight against a gang of inbred cannibals in the desert.

During the simulation, the Hansens said they were groped in a sexual manner, slapped, and made to commit violent acts against the actors in order to survive the night.

In one sequence, Tom was forced to defend himself against a performer who carried a machete and wore a sleeveless buckskin suit.

The man chased Tom down a narrow passage of rock formations, boxing him into a tight corner. The man then lunged at Tom, swiping the air with the machete and spewing saliva from his mouth, according to the police report.

"I really thought he was going to kill me," Tom said. "I began swinging my fists, punching and kicking him. His body leaned up against mine, and his skin was slick with some kind of oil. He told me things he wanted to do to Jennifer while I watched. Then he tried to lick me. I think it was at that point that I screamed."

But the most sickening moment came later in the night, when Tom stumbled into a sand cave to find his wife pinned to the ground by two men in monster makeup.

Jennifer was screaming to be let go, her coat flung wide, her blouse clawed open to expose her undergarments, and at least one piece of jewelry stripped from her body.

Tom said that one of the men was naked, straddling his wife and pressing a large hunting knife to her cheek. The second man crouched nearby in the dirt, blowing spit bubbles into his hand and fondling his crotch area.

"I don't know how else to say this," Tom explained, "but the man was visibly aroused, grinding against Jennifer and shouting what sounded like a voodoo incantation. He was…he was *slobbering* on her. My wife started to cry, slapping the man's hands away, but the man didn't stop."

At that moment, Tom said, the tattooed woman shambled into the cave like a walking corpse, her face dotted in bulbous cysts and puckered lesions that looked scaly to the touch. She wore a brown sackcloth dress cut open to her navel, the flimsy material blackened with grime.

While Tom and Jennifer watched in horror, the woman performed some kind of deranged dance ritual, gyrating to the sound of distant drums, masturbating, and working herself into a sexual frenzy. The sackcloth fell to her waist, exposing her naked breasts and belly. The woman then came after Tom, licking her blistered lips and panting like a heat-stricken dog.

"When she touched me her skin was brittle, powdery, like a mummy or a dead body," Tom described with escalating terror. "And she reeked of cheap booze. The stench was coming off of her in waves."

According to the police report, the woman pinned Tom against a rock wall and tried to force him to suckle her breast. When Tom resisted, the woman slashed at Tom with a knife and fought to pull him out of the cave. Desperate, Tom struck the woman with his flashlight so that he could rescue his wife from the two men.

"I hit her once across the face, hard, and blood began dripping from her nose," Tom reported. "She fell onto the ground and began laughing—this shrieking, high-pitched laughter that sliced through my ears like a razor. Then she began smearing the blood all over her face and body."

Tom said that as he dragged his wife away from the mutant-men, the tattooed woman hiked up her tatty dress, squatted like a frog, and began to urinate in the dirt. "Drink with us!" the woman croaked, using her hands to splash her liquid waste onto the Hansens. "Taste it, fuckers! Taste my filth!"

Tom said the woman then charged at the couple, her private parts exposed and her swollen tongue drooping from her mouth.

Terrified, the Hansens ran from the cave and searched for an exit in the dark. During their flight they stumbled across other guests being held hostage by the actors, including one woman trapped inside a zippered body bag and a man bound with rope to an enormous wooden crucifix.

By the time the Hansens found an escape route, hidden beneath thick camouflage netting, they were cold, filthy, and exhausted.

Fearing for their safety if they returned to the entrance to demand their money back, Tom and Jennifer drove to a service road where they could get reception and called the Indio County Sheriff's Office on their cell phone. The next day they sought legal counsel and filed the lawsuit soon after.

Bobby Pruitt has refused to speak to the press about the incident, though an inside source reports that he is considering filing a counter suit against Mr. Hansen for his attack on the female actress during the simulation.

Mr. Pruitt's attorney, Ross A. Callan, has said there have been no other complaints about "Personal Demons" and that all participants must sign a liability waiver before the simulation begins.

"This is a young, newly-married couple who are trying to make money off their supposed suffering," he said. "In reality, they knew exactly what they bought tickets for, and we have their signatures on the dotted line to prove it."

"Personal Demons" will be closed this weekend as the Indio County Sheriff's Office investigates the claims of the Hansens and determines what illegalities took place at the event.

"I'll be amazed if the police don't close that place down and arrest everybody involved," Tom Hansen said.

He stressed that the experience was particularly agonizing for his wife, who now suffers from heart palpitations and anxiety, according to her husband.

"This has been a living nightmare for us," said Tom. "It was like a real-life death match out there."

INDIO—The boyfriend of a 37-year-old woman found dead in the Indio desert said the deceased was "a beautiful, loving spirit" and the "victim of an inhumane and savage attack."

A backpacker returning to his campsite discovered the body in a field beyond Cranterford Road on Saturday night.

Observing that the woman wasn't moving and had deep wounds on her face and neck, the backpacker rushed to a call box on Cranterford Road and called 911.

Investigators said that the deceased appeared to have been the victim of a violent beating. The case is now being investigated as a homicide, said a spokesperson for the Indio Police Department.

The victim has been identified as Tiffany Cobb, an exotic dancer from Los Angeles.

Cobb was an adventurous woman who had devoted her life to the creative arts, according to Bobby Pruitt, the victim's partner of more than 20 years. Pruitt, 38, said that Cobb had been working in his experimental haunted attraction called "Personal Demons" at the time of her death.

News affiliate KMIR reported that "Personal Demons" is an outdoor simulation in which participants are made to feel trapped inside their own live-action horror movie.

According to an online source, the controversial experience involves violence, simulated torture, and murder "scenes" in which Cobb terrorized and assaulted the customers.

"Tiffany used experimental performance as a form of self-expression," Pruitt, who has produced haunted attractions for several years, told KMIR. "But someone who attended the event on the night she disappeared didn't care about her art. He was only there to hurt her."

Over the past several days, law enforcement has kept the scene secure while searching the site for clues. The area is described by police as "vast and open, with no single entrance or exit," making the investigation difficult and time-consuming.

"The event that the victim was performing in didn't have one primary location, one specific area for us to focus on. It was a very chaotic night when she went missing, and there was limited security and an unprepared emergency team," said Indio's Chief of Police Joe Martinez.

"We're putting the pieces together," added Chief Martinez. "Who attended the event, the people last seen with the victim, who the other performers were. This was a savage crime, and we won't stop looking for the perpetrator."

Cobb went missing sometime on Friday evening during a late-night performance of "Personal Demons," according to police. Her body, savagely beaten and hidden by desert moss and chaparral, was found late on Saturday night.

Chief Martinez said the murder may have been a result of "a reckless experiment that got out of hand," but also suggested the possibility that Cobb was the intended target all along.

According to the crime scene description, the victim had been punched, kicked, and stomped to death. There was no evidence of sexual assault, although the body had been stripped nude and posed in a lewd position.

Law enforcement also confirmed that pages from the Bible had been crumpled and lodged inside the victim's throat.

"In recent months, Ms. Cobb had received notoriety in the underground press and horror community, and dangerous people may have been drawn to that," the police chief said. "She had been threatened online and someone may have intentionally gone to the desert to harm her. They certainly went to great lengths to hide the body."

The isolated field where police came upon the body remained cordoned off with yellow barrier tape Sunday morning as officers canvassed the area.

Though a housing development has opened up on Cranterford Road, Chief Martinez believes the perpetrator is most likely someone who attended the performance.

"I don't think someone left their house, walked into the desert, and found a woman to attack and kill. This is a stable community, a safe area," said Chief Martinez. "I'm convinced this was done by someone with easy access to the victim and who had an ax to grind."

The exact cause of death has not been determined but an autopsy is scheduled.

From *Christened in Blood: Cherie Alvarez and the Apple Hill Slayings* (p. 121-123):

No one can say exactly what Bobby Pruitt had in mind on the night of the Apple Hill killings, though he had been stalking Cherie Alvarez for at least three months before the attack, studying her routines and monitoring her activity at San Jose State University. But to conduct a mission of such misguided revenge would have been an insurmountable task for one person. Like Charles Manson before him, Pruitt used suggestibility and coercion to conduct surveillance on Alvarez and to assault her and her friends on that horrific summer night. The ex-cons, Clive Langer and Colin Moore, had already performed violent acts on women inside "Death Rituals" and "Personal Demons," and they were more than eager to take their abusive proclivities into the real world of flesh and blood. To Langer and Moore, Pruitt was a powerful authority figure who respected them and listened to them. In turn, they were willing to follow his lead no matter the cost.

Pruitt's history of juvenile crime and undisciplined creativity made him an attractive and esoteric figure in the eyes of his two followers. Lance Berryman, who interviewed Pruitt for a blog about the Halloween industry, believed there was something enigmatic about his presence, something furtive, a "mocking magic" that drew people in. "He had a charisma about him, a sort of beautiful derangement, that at one time even I found appealing," Berryman admitted. And the unsolved murder of Tiffany Cobb only added to Pruitt's quixotic and enduring allure. He used her death to make Langer and Moore believe he was a pitiable but righteous man whose reprisal against Cherie was entirely justified.

"Bobby had made a number of enemies over the years, especially in his younger days, a fact which I believe led directly to Tiffany's murder," Berryman said. "Maybe a jilted lover, or a man maliciously wronged…someone who really wanted them both to suffer." But Berryman was quick to point out that Pruitt was too narrow-minded to accept that stark reality. "Bobby was irrational and obsessive, consumed with the here and now. And in his twisted way of looking at the world, Cherie Alvarez was his enemy—the root of his downfall, the spark of his madness."

As part of his ill-considered plan, Pruitt encouraged Langer and Moore to revel in their criminal pasts. With jargon (what Berryman has since described as "intellectual mumbo-jumbo") he picked up during his stint in a juvenile detention facility, he spoke passionately of warranted violence, felon disenfranchisement, and the transcendence of anything ordinary and prosaic. He flattered his acolytes constantly, praising their ability to evoke genuine terror in the people who attended "Death Rituals" and "Personal Demons." In both attractions, Langer tied up women with rope, tormented them with live insects, and groped their genitals. Moore delighted in body shaming, rape and death threats, and physical assault. After Tiffany was killed, and at the insistence of Pruitt, the pair made several trips to the San Francisco Bay Area, including one pivotal visit to San Jose State in the spring of 2016. There, after breaking into Cherie Alvarez's truck, they set off a terrifying chain of events that would shock and captivate the entire country...

By most accounts, Pruitt wanted revenge against Cherie Alvarez, whom he viewed as responsible for exposing the truth behind "Death Rituals" and subjecting Tiffany to online threats and real danger. That George Matthews, the journalist from *The National Dish*, was actually the one to reveal Cobb's personal history to the public was either unimportant to Pruitt or suggestive of a veiled vengeance that was far more depraved. Pruitt had spent the majority of his life constructing simulated horror scenes featuring special effects, large-scale props, and other tools of illusion. In the months leading up to the atrocities at the Apple Hill cabin, perhaps he had something more palpable in mind, something mortal and concrete, something with a little meat on its bones...

Berryman offered this more direct explanation of the motives behind the Apple Hill raid: "Bobby hated women. He had a lifelong habit of blaming other people for his failings and he cowered away from men in positions of power. He focused his attention on Cherie because he thought he could win. He thought he could destroy her the way he had been destroyed. But Bobby was shortsighted in his visions. He no idea what was in store for him."

SAN JOSE—An end-of-the-year celebration for the Theater and Film program at San Jose State University turned into an unfortunate evening of vandalism and property destruction.

As students and faculty enjoyed food and beverages inside the lobby of the Audrey Hall Theater, one of the school's security guards entered the room to announce that several cars in the east parking lot had been scratched, dented, and smashed.

"We were there to celebrate all our department accomplished this year, including several student-produced films and stage shows," said Katie Morrison, an adjunct drama professor and director.

After receiving an urgent call from the campus security guard, police found 6 damaged vehicles Saturday night in the parking lot at the school. Outdoor security lights had also been shattered, most likely to give the perpetrators the cover of darkness, said Officer Josephine Blair of the San Jose Police Department.

The vandalized cars had been scratched by keys, sharp rocks, or perhaps even a knife, according to Morrison, who surveyed the damage.

"It happened when we were all inside," Morrison said. "The people who did it must have known the lot would be deserted during the party. They were watching us, waiting for the right time."

Morrison's racing-green MGB roadster was smashed hood to rear with a rock, while one student's red Ford truck had been broken into, the driver's window shattered and the upholstery torn up with what must have been a large knife.

"It's my father's house-painting truck. He uses it for work," the freshman student said. She also reported to police that her purse and daily planner were stolen from the vehicle.

Other cars had profanity and even threats scratched into their hoods and doors, Morrison said.

"It's more than disconcerting," said Morrison, who has taught at the university for 8 years. "This wasn't just a prank—not with the damage that was done and the curse words they scratched onto the cars."

Officer Blair was not able to provide an estimate of total damages, but she said that the extent of the vandalism was not her only focus.

"We've interviewed the students whose vehicles were targeted," Officer Blair said. "At least one student reported that she felt like she was being followed days before the incident, which suggests that this was a planned attack. That dangerous weapons were used to inflict the damage has law enforcement equally concerned."

Morrison disagreed, saying that she does not believe the vandalism was connected specifically to the Theater and Film department, or that her students were targeted on purpose.

Meanwhile, the students whose cars were damaged are looking forward to putting the incident behind them and beginning their summer vacation.

"It was a bad way to start our vacation, but it's time to have fun with our friends and enjoy this great California weather," said the student whose truck was vandalized.

APPLE HILL – Original Story (Foothill 7 TV, 7:30 a.m. on May 20, 2016):

Several people are reportedly dead at a cabin home in Apple Hill, California.

KCRA, the news affiliate in El Dorado County, reports that California BCI is sending an "all-inclusive team" to the scene.

According to the spokesperson for California BCI, the victims, both male and female, were found dead at a vacation rental property on Stone County Road east of Placerville, off Highway 50.

Aerial footage captured by KCRA shows police officers and several cruisers parked on a dirt road near the home, sectioned off by yellow cordon. A canine unit was spotted at the scene.

No other information has been released.

We have a crew headed to the scene of the crime.

Stay tuned to Foothill 7 TV for more information.

Update (8:15 a.m.):

The El Dorado County, California sheriff is expected to make an official statement soon regarding a multiple homicide scene that was discovered this morning in Apple Hill.

According to reports, six people were killed with a gun, knives, and other sharp instruments.

The murders took place sometime during the night yesterday, in an isolated cabin on Stone County Road, off highway 50.

Dr. Gary Springer of Apple Hill Community Center says that none of the victims are related but that at least two of them are young women.

Dr. Springer adds that a vehicle was found parked outside the cabin, its driver's side window sprayed with blood.

The nearby High Hill Ranch School has been closed for the day. Traffic is currently closed going in and out of the scene.

At this time, law enforcement has not commented on a suspect in the case.

We have a crew on scene. Stay tuned to Foothill 7 TV for more information and visit our website for the latest news.

Update (9:00 a.m.):

El Dorado County Sheriff Doug Gladstone says that at least five people are dead in a home-invasion-style crime scene in Apple Hill, California.

In an interview with Foothill 7 TV on Sunday morning, Sheriff Gladstone stated that investigators are still unsure if the suspect or suspects are among the deceased.

Detectives and a canine unit are currently searching the wooded area for clues.

Initial reports early Sunday morning were that six adults, both male and female, were found slain in and outside of a remote cabin in the forests of Apple Hill.

Foothill 7 TV can now report that five victims, three males and two females, were discovered at the scene. Another woman survived the attack. She was found in a closet in the back of the cabin, her face bruised and her clothes soaked in blood.

The names of the victims or perpetrators have not been released, but Sheriff Gladstone stated that the vacation cabin was owned by the Green family of Northern California.

Sheriff Gladstone indicated that two of the deceased were college students from the Bay Area.

More information is expected to be released in the afternoon hours.

Update (2:15 p.m.):

"We are no longer actively pursuing a suspect. We have come to understand that there were three assailants involved in this attack, and all three of them have been pronounced deceased at the scene."

These were the sobering words from El Dorado County Sheriff Doug Gladstone on Sunday afternoon.

Five people were found mutilated, stabbed, and beaten to death in a vicious home-invasion attack on Saturday night.

According to a police report released this afternoon, one of the female victims was found in the kitchen, her throat savagely cut.

A man was discovered on the floor next to her, stabbed to death.

There are other victims and at least one female survivor, but police have not provided further details from the scene.

Sheriff Gladstone said that the victims have not been identified yet, but that at least one of them is a member of the Green family, who owns the property.

The sheriff added that the surviving victim, a college-age female, was in a state of shock, had severe injuries, and was taken immediately to a hospital in Placerville.

"It's early in the investigation, but we have a task force putting a timeline of events together. It appears that three young women were staying in the cabin, and that three male assailants invaded the home with the intention of terrorizing them. From there, we have a long road to go in terms of understanding everything that transpired," Sheriff Gladstone said.

Video footage by KCRA indicates that this is an active crime scene with heavy foot traffic and a strong police presence. Two vans from the El Dorado County Coroner's Office have just departed the scene, presumably with the victims of the slayings inside.

"We have investigators at the hospital, just waiting for the doctors to give the go-ahead to speak with the surviving girl," Sheriff Gladstone said. "She's very lucky to be alive."

KULCHNER PRODUCTIONS presents

A SPARK TV NETWORK TELEVISION EVENT

"The Apple Hill Murders"

Written by Brant Kulchner and Prairie Williams
Produced by Brant Kulcher and Elaine Moody
Originally aired December 15, 2016 - 21:00 ET

NOTE TO READER: To distinguish between past and present, the archived video and interview materials have all been noted in this text as "archived footage." All present-day footage has been noted as "narrative footage."

(REENACTMENT OVER CREDITS): *A high-angle shot of a white, four-door jeep moving along the road. The sky is eggshell blue. Mountains capped with snow in the background. The route passes through conifer forests and apple orchards—"God's country."*

Inside the jeep: PAULA GREEN, 20, driving, eyes hidden behind mirrored sunglasses. CORAL HARRINGTON, 19, sitting in the passenger seat, thumbing through a magazine. CHERIE ALVAREZ, 18, in the backseat, admiring the scenery through the open window.

Through CHERIE'S POV: an art gallery called "Gold Rush Paintings"; a fruit stand; a market and deli; a gas station, "Ernie's Gas N' Snack"; a tavern, "El Dorado Brewery."

The jeep exits the highway and follows several narrow roads until it turns onto a switchback. The vehicle then pulls into a crushed-stone driveway and stops in front of a log cabin. In the hills behind the cabin, treetops stretch on for miles.

A MEDIUM shot of the cabin, secluded, rustic, and somewhat forlorn. Windows dusted with yellow pollen. Star-shaped Christmas lights and a rooster weathervane on the roof. A wilted wreath on the front door. Unpruned fruit trees surround the property like sentinels.

CUT TO:

(REENACTMENT): *A 911 OPERATOR sits at a wrap-around cockpit of computer screens and blinking phone lines.*

911 OPERATOR: What's your emergency?

CALLER: Yeah, I'm calling from my cell phone on Stone County Road. I was dirt-biking when I saw something outside one of the cabins in the woods. A man fallen against a car. He was covered in blood!

911 OPERATOR: Was the man breathing, sir?

CALLER: I don't know—I just biked out on the road until I got reception—but it didn't look like it. There's a lot of blood, on his shirt and face, on the car. He was slouched there. I think he was dead!

911 OPERATOR: And where exactly are you calling from, sir?

CALLER: I told you, I'm on Stone County Road in Apple Hill, about a half-mile from the cabin. It's small, with Christmas lights on the roof. Two cars out front. You need to send someone quick. There's trouble in that house...

(ARCHIVED FOOTAGE): A NEWS REPORTER stands in front of the cabin in Apple Hill, its perimeter cordoned off with yellow tape; behind him, police cruisers, DETECTIVES huddled by the door, one of them with a digital camera looped around his neck.

NEWS REPORTER: Today, in this scenic cabin nestled in the Sierra foothills of Northern California, police are in the process of removing several bodies after a home invasion leaves two women and three men dead. In a surprising twist, the suspects are thought to be among the deceased in what police are calling a "horrific attack that spun wildly out of control." One of many questions on the minds of everyone at the crime scene this afternoon: who are all the victims, and why did this happen to them?

(NARRATIVE FOOTAGE)

MEDIUM shots of the mountain highway; the winery at Apple Hill Farms; a basket of ripe apples; a farmer's market; a lake streaked with blue and green hues.

MALE CUSTOMER, *standing outside a country store, carrying a bag of groceries.* There's so much to do in this little town of ours. There's hay rides, pony rides, a cider press, orchards and fruit farms. One ranch has a miniature train and a corn maze for kids. Fishing ponds, hot apple donuts, horseback rides, and wineries for grown-ups. We're about an hour's drive from Sacramento, our state capital. It's a very quiet place to live and earn an honest living.

FEMALE CUSTOMER, *bagging blueberries at the farmer's market.* Most people visit us on their way to Lake Tahoe. We're just a dot on the map, but Apple Hill has its own school, a few country stores, and some of the most beautiful Christmas tree farms in the world. We're a tight-knit community here, and it's a great place to live or vacation.

(ARCHIVED FOOTAGE): *The News Reporter now stands between two vehicles parked near the cabin. One of the cars is the white jeep, its driver's side door and window spattered with blood. The other, several yards away, is a tan-colored Buick Regal. A FORENSIC TECHNICIAN kneels beside the jeep, dusting for fingerprints.*

NEWS REPORTER: Returning to tonight's top story, two young women and three men are dead, slashed to ribbons, after a home invasion in the quiet town of Apple Hill. According to early reports, the suspects raided the cabin in the dead of night, catching the women by surprise. Police say the murder weapons, including a kitchen knife and a metal skewer, all came from inside the residence, leading investigators to believe the suspects did not go there with the intent to kill.

SUBTITLE: "The Apple Hill Murders"

SUBTITLE: "The following program features a combination of dramatic reenactments, voiceovers, still photographs, and archived and narrative footage. Certain images and details may have been altered. It is intended for mature audiences. Viewer discretion is advised."

(NARRATIVE FOOTAGE)

J. GREEN: It didn't register with me, what the police officer was saying, the details of the crime, and what happened to the girls. His words went through me like air. But my mind cleared when he said Paula was dead—but that she fought back before she died. He had my attention after that. The first thing I did, after I hung up the phone, was call my parents in San Francisco.

SAMUEL GREEN, *Paula Green's father, served as a test and evaluation officer for the Navy Theater Ballistic Missile Defense program. Now 62, he is retired from the military.* Jennifer was in hysterics. She told us everything she knew—that Paula and another friend had been killed, but that Cherie was still alive, that she had escaped or hid in the cabin, she wasn't sure. Cherie was in a hospital in Placerville, and we just drove there right away. We had only met her once before, but we had to invest our energy into something. We were happy she was alive, but we went to the hospital so we wouldn't go crazy. We had to have something to do.

They let us see her—her father was there with her. She was beaten badly, and she apologized for not saving our daughter.

MARY GREEN, *Paula Green's mother, a homemaker and former ballet dancer. She is 58.* We told her she had nothing to apologize for. We were thankful she was alive and that she was a good friend to Paula, and that she was there—

S. GREEN: That she was there when Paula died, and that they didn't give in to these men. That they fought for their lives and one of them survived.

J. GREEN: My sister was a very good dancer and actress. She loved the stage, had all the leads in the school plays and dance ensembles. That's actually how she met Cherie and Coral. They had written a play at San Jose State and they were going to perform it for the school, and Paula had gotten the lead role. I remember how proud they all were of the project, because it was produced entirely by women, and they had done it all themselves.

(ARCHIVED FOOTAGE): *Inside the Audrey Hall Theater at San Jose State University. Final curtain call. Cast and crew onstage, including Cherie Alvarez, Coral Harrington, and Paula Green. As the applause dies down, someone hands Cherie a microphone...*

CHERIE ALVAREZ: First, thank you to our wonderful audience tonight, and all our past audiences—you guys have been so supportive of what we have tried to accomplish with this play. I want to thank Katie Morrison, our director, and Coral Harrington, my best friend and writing partner. Everyone on set design, our entire cast and crew, the school band—and a special thank you to Paula Green, who took our script and gave it life...

(ARCHIVED FOOTAGE) KCRA NEWSROOM: *A NEWS ANCHOR with an earpiece and papers on the desk before him. In the upper left corner of the screen, a photograph of the cabin in Apple Hill. The horizontal ticker reads: "NORTHERN CALIFORNIA BLOOD-BATH."*

NEWS ANCHOR: Joining us right now is Sheriff Doug Gladstone of the El Dorado County Police Department. Thank you for this interview, Sheriff Gladstone, during what surely is a stressful and busy time.

Now a SPLIT SCREEN, the news anchor on the left, SHERIFF DOUG GLADSTONE on the right.

SHERIFF DOUG GLADSTONE, *a 25-year veteran of the El Dorado County Sheriff's Office. He is 49.* Thank you for having me.

NEWS ANCHOR: Sheriff, we've received conflicting reports from our boots on the ground in Apple Hill. Can you clarify a few points for us? Paula Green, a 20-year-old college student, was the first victim police discovered in the cabin. Who killed her and how exactly did she die?

GLADSTONE: Based on the evidence, Ms. Green most likely died from trauma to her neck, but I can't say more until we get the autopsy results. Next to her was the body of one of the suspects, and right now we're going on the assumption that he was the man who murdered Ms. Green.

(NARRATIVE FOOTAGE)

Jennifer Green sits at her desk, several news articles in front of her. CLOSE SHOT on the headlines: "MULTIPLE SLAYINGS IN MOUNTAIN CABIN," "SADISTIC NORTHERN CALIFORNIA MURDERS."

J. GREEN: This has been so hard on my parents—in many ways, the less they know about how Paula died, the better. They've lost one of their daughters. That's going to haunt them for the rest of their lives. But I'm an archivist by profession. My job is to document and understand the details of every little thing. I want to know why those men went to our cabin. I want to know why Colin Moore killed my sister.

RICKY SHELDON, *35, the author of* CHRISTENED IN BLOOD: CHERIE ALVAREZ AND THE APPLE HILL MURDERS: Colin Moore was scum. There's no other way to put it. Usually, when I write a true-crime book, I try to find some decency in the bad guy, a shred of humanity, something from his past that the reader can empathize with. But Colin Moore was an abusive prick. Okay, he was a father— to a daughter, a nice kid. She's 16 now. That's the one good thing you could say about him.

Moore's record of domestic violence goes back a long way. He beat up at least one ex-girlfriend that we know of, along with the mother of his child. He stalked them, car-prowled them, and threatened them by phone and letter. He served five years in state prison for domestic assault before going to work for Bobby Pruitt. The guy was a low-life and highly suggestible. More than likely he followed Pruitt around like a dog starving for attention.

But I don't believe he went to the cabin to kill Paula. His track record doesn't support that level of violence. But he was there to rough her up, and things took a nasty turn. The assailants had no idea that the girls were not going to go down easy.

SHANAMARIE MOORE, *16, sits on the stoop outside an apartment building. Her youthful beauty belies a background of poverty and hard times. A bad-apple kid but with a good heart.* I never really knew my dad growing up. He would show up sometimes, out of nowhere, and take me to the park or to Burger King. But he was a mean person. He went to jail for hitting my mom, and he would write to me from jail, these long letters, but I never wrote him back. If you hurt my mom, that's it. I'm done with you, even if you are my blood.

When my mom told me about what happened—well, it didn't surprise me. And I'm not sad that he's dead, not really, except now I'll never know why he did what he did, if he chose to go to the cabin or if he was forced by someone else. My mom told me that my dad was always being tricked by bad people into doing bad things.

Those girls weren't that much older than me—and I wonder if my dad was thinking about me when he was hurting them.

(REENACTMENT): *Nighttime. The cabin in Apple Hill shrouded in late-spring mist. The rooster weathervane creaks in the wind; the Christmas lights blink from the roof; and in the darkening sky above, the moon shines a vibrant shade of orange.*

GLADSTONE (VOICEOVER NARRATION): In these parts, it's a myth that no one locks their doors. Apple Hill might be a small town, but the people aren't stupid. Best we can put together, the other two waited in the Buick and let Colin Moore do the work. He unscrewed the porch light and folded a towel over the doorknob. One crack with the hammer and he was in. And right there he found Paula Green sleeping on the couch.

(REENACTMENT CONT.): *Paula Green, sleeping on the couch in the front room of the cabin. An afghan blanket draped over her lower body. A braided rug covers the floor. The walls are decorated with rustic tractor parts and antique fox-hunting paintings.*

A door creaks. A long, slinking shadow passes over the wall. Boots scuff on the floor.

Across from the couch, near the door, COLIN MOORE, 30s, watches Paula sleep. He is short, runt-skinny, with a craggy face and thin ginger hair. He wears a garrison fatigue jacket and grease-spotted blue jeans.

Moore creeps to the couch, but freezes when Paula turns over in her sleep, her back now to him.

Her can see her rear end, clad in sheer panties. Moore gets excited...

(NARRATIVE FOOTAGE)

GLADSTONE: He came with a mask, zip-ties, and a handkerchief for a gag. The micro-hammer was clipped to his belt. He was going to have some fun with her while the other girls slept. But Moore didn't count on what happened next.

(REENACTMENT CONT.): *Ogling Paula's body, Moore reaches inside his shirt and tweaks one of his nipples. He gasps at the sudden pleasure. He then slides on his disguise—a plastic Oliver Hardy mask, complete with a red bulbous nose and a bowler hat.*

Slowly, Moore slips the zip-ties from his pocket. Grips them in one hand. With his free hand he now holds the handkerchief. He wraps it around his knuckles and inches to the couch. He's breathing heavily—almost panting.

CUT TO:

(REENACTMENT CONT.): *The camera pans along the dirt road outside the cabin, past the jeep to the Buick Regal parked a short distance away. Inside the car two glowing orange embers give off a pinch of light. Through the hazy blue cigarette smoke we see:*

CLIVE LANGER, 40s, in the passenger seat: a giant man with a bowling-ball head and a lantern jaw. He wears filthy bib overalls with a soiled wife-beater underneath. His enormous thighs jitter with excitement.

In the driver's seat: BOBBY PRUITT, 38, scrawny and angular, his plum-dark eyes brimming with hatred. Dressed in black denim and black driving gloves, Pruitt stares out the windshield.

LANGER: I fuckin' hate waiting.

PRUITT: Just do what I tell you. We have our fun and split like we were never here.

CLOSE SHOT of the Pruitt's gloved hand. It clutches a daily planner with a skull-patterned cover.

(NARRATIVE FOOTAGE)

GLADSTONE: The assailants wanted to draw the experience out into one long night of terror. Like what you might see in a horror movie, they fantasized about what it would be like to toy with these women. Moore and Langer had gotten the data they needed after breaking into Cherie's car and stealing her purse. The killers knew her schedule and the address of the cabin.

A few days after the break-in at the college, the girls hit the road for summer vacation. On the morning of the killings, the assailants were seen pumping gas in Placerville, so they were in the area before the girls arrived in Apple Hill. They probably watched the residence. Watched them drive in and get set up. Watched them go to the country store and buy groceries...

(REENACTMENT): *Cherie, Coral, and Paula wandering the aisles of a Mom-and-Pop country store, tossing chips, beer, chicken filets, and hot peppers into their cart...*

GLADSTONE (VOICEOVER NARRATION): They watched from the woods. We found bags of beef jerky and empty beer cans up on the hillside. They could see right into the windows of the cabin...

(REENACTMENT CONT.): *The girls in the kitchen, drinking and laughing as they cook fajita kebabs. A cast-iron skillet sizzles and catches fire, spiraling smoke in the air. Playful shrieks as they try to douse the fire with beer, which only makes the problem worse...*

(REENACTMENT CONT.): *Later, in the living room of the cabin, the girls are playing the board game CLUE. Laughing. Talking. An old horror movie plays on the television set.*

GLADSTONE (VOICEOVER NARRATION): These men had patience. They waited until late. Until the girls had gone to sleep. Moore cut the lights and the phone line, and then he busted the lock. Based on the order of events that transpired, we don't think he was supposed to go inside by himself. But the man was a degenerate. He couldn't control himself.

(REENACTMENT CONT.): *Moore hovering above Paula. He leans in close. He nuzzles the cracked plastic of the mask against her ear.*

MOORE: Wake up, you skinny bitch.

Like water bursting from a dam, Paula lurches awake, startling Moore before he can wrap the handkerchief around her mouth. CRACK! Her elbow connects forcefully with his jaw, sending him toppling onto his ass.

Paula spins off the couch, knocking over a small table as she darts for the kitchen. She heads for the dish rack, where a large chopping knife has been left to dry. She grabs it, whirls around—

Just as Moore smashes the side of her head with the cast-iron skillet that had been on the stove. Paula drops. The knife skids across the floor.

Paula at the edge of consciousness, blood streaked across her forehead. Enraged, Moore rips his mask away and approaches with the skillet. He raises the metal pan with two hands above his head, then brings it down hard onto Paula's mid-section. She screams in pain.

CUT TO:

(REENACTMENT CONT.): *Inside the Buick, Pruitt and Langer react to the scream, ditching their smokes out the window.*

PRUITT: Fuck!

LANGER: What'd we do now?

PRUITT: Glass door in back. Put your mask on and go. And don't let them get away.

LANGER: What're you gonna do?

PRUITT: Someone's gotta stay with the car. We can handle this. Now go.

Clutching his mask to his chest, Langer exits the car and plods toward the back of the cabin. He walks with a bow-legged tilt, the rocky ground crunching under his heavy boots.

Inside the car, Pruitt takes a large swig from a bottle of whiskey.

(REENACTMENT CONT.): *Moore pacing the kitchen in a panic. Paula tries to call out, but she can only muster a hacking cough. Still, she reaches for the fallen knife...*

MOORE, *a nervous wreck*: Stop that. Don't do that.

Paula inches toward the knife. She's almost got it.

MOORE: I don't wanna hurt you again.

Paula's fingers close over the handle of the knife.

MOORE: Shit, I told you don't do that! Stop it!

Moore pulls back with the skillet, then cracks Paula across the knees. Bones crunch. She wails in agony.

MOORE: All I was gonna do was tie you up, goddammit! Shut up. Shut up!

Like a child throwing a tantrum, he hurls the skillet onto the floor.

MOORE: Aw, shit! Now what I am gonna do?

Moore turns to flee and finds himself face to face with Cherie Alvarez, who plunges a metal kabob skewer into his chest.

Before he can grasp what's happened, Moore unhooks the hammer from his belt and wallops Cherie across the face with it. She crashes against the counter.

At that moment, Paula sits up and drives the chopping knife deep into Moore's hamstring.

Screaming, Moore drops the hammer. He reaches back and yanks the knife from out his thigh. Blood sprays in a circular arc as Moore whips around. Knife swinging, the skewer still lodged in his chest, he leaps onto Paula.

(ARCHIVED FOOTAGE): *Inside THE NATIONAL DISH newsroom, a BUSTY FEMALE REPORTER, 20s, stands before the camera.*

BUSTY FEMALE REPORTER: Cherie Alvarez—a hero who acted in self-defense to protect herself and her friends, or a homicidal thrill-killer with a deeply rooted desire to hurt others? A young woman who spoke out against bullying and violent behavior all of her life—only to become a blood-hungry vigilante? These are the big questions that the dedicated journalists here at *The National Dish* headquarters are asking tonight.

Those close to the Apple Hill Murders case claim that the 18-year-old damsel-in-distress had been fantasizing about killing for years, especially after her own mother was so viciously slaughtered by deranged mental patient Alfred Mitchell. Especially after all those years she spent as a victim of schoolyard bullying.

Did Cherie somehow will her psychological distress into bloody reality? Did those men deserve to die? And let's not forget the most important question at hand: is murder acceptable when committed in self-defense?

No matter how you interpret her actions, clearly something inside Cherie snapped, unleashing a maelstrom of madness on that gruesome summer night in the woods. Did she plan the bloodshed that erupted in Paula Green's cabin? Most likely not—but she certainly didn't hesitate to attack either, slashing her way to survival while blood ran in rivers at her feet...

(NARRATIVE FOOTAGE)

GLADSTONE: I don't doubt that Cherie experienced some kind of psychological shock that night. But if you see your friend being hurt, if you think your life is on the line, you're going to react in one of two ways. You're either going to run, or you're going to stay and fight. And Cherie stayed. And she fought. She fought harder than anyone I've seen in my 25 years of law enforcement.

Now, I wouldn't be surprised if she slipped into a dissociated state at the time of the killings—a frame of mind where her feelings cut off from her actions. That I might agree with. But take one look at the way this young lady chose to live her life—she always looked the other way. Always saw the good in other people. She's not a vigilante. She's not even "the woman who was pushed too far." She's just a person. A person who came across some bad men. A person who wanted to live rather than die.

(REENACTMENT): *As Moore collapses onto Paula, she grips the metal skewer with both hands, using it as a lever. It digs deep into his sternum, tearing through the thick meat of his chest. Moore screams, but he still manages to overpower her.*

Paula continues to drive the skewer into Moore's chest—it's either him or her. Moaning in horror, Moore pushes the knife into the side of her throat.

Paula's body slackens. Moore drags the knife across her throat in a jagged motion, severing her windpipe and arteries. Blood gushes over Moore's hands and onto the floor.

MOORE: You made me do this, you rotten bitch! This is your fault! All your fault!

PHWUMP! Cherie has just kicked Moore squarely in the groin from behind.

He flops onto his side on the floor, howling in pain, one hand clutching his balls, the other hand gripping the metal skewer embedded in his chest.

Cherie's POV – she sees Paula dead on the floor, a pool of blood forming around her head.

MOORE, *his voice a rusty croak*: There are others…coming for you.

Cherie steps forward. Wearing a "Night of the Living Dead" T-shirt and black shorts, she looks like an angel of death.

In one graceful move, Cherie wrenches the skewer from Moore's chest and rams it into his Adam's apple. As blood bubbles up from his mouth, Cherie rips the weapon out of Moore's throat, raises it above her shoulder, and plunges it back into his neck. Blood sprays her face. Moore gasps for air, eyes bulging, legs kicking wildly. Cherie raises the skewer a third time…

(REENACTMENT CONT.): *The moon looms large over the property. From deep in the woods comes a dog's mournful howl. Then—the sound of branches and twigs snapping underfoot.*

Langer lumbers along to the back of the cabin, a coil of rope on his studded belt. The plastic mask—a devil with rainbow-colored horns—barely fits over his enormous face.

(NARRATIVE FOOTAGE)

SHELDON: Clive Langer was a monster. A big, bald-headed monster. He was also a former bodybuilder and steroid junkie. His rap sheet was overrun with violent crimes, burglaries, armed robbery, assault and battery. He served 10 years for involuntary manslaughter after he beat a woman to death outside of a bar in Boyle Heights. Caved in half her skull. But the prosecution bungled the case and cut a deal with the defense, so Langer got a light sentence. The woman was his ex-girlfriend. She had already filed two restraining orders against the piece of shit.

JASMINE VERBENA, *42, is a sexual assault and domestic violence counselor at the Safe Haven Women's Shelter in Los Angeles.* Her name was Olivia Lucero. She had come to Safe Haven at least four times before her death, usually with her face bruised up or her lip split open. She was looking for a place to hide. She said that her ex-boyfriend was following her. Breaking into her apartment and hitting her. One time the beating was so bad, he ruptured her liver. And the police never did anything about it.

Olivia wanted to get more involved in the domestic violence community. She had asked me how to become a counselor at Safe

Haven. But then came the night at the bar. He was waiting for her in the parking lot, crouched behind her car like an animal. He had seen her dancing with another man, and he wasn't going to allow her to get away with that.

He despised women—it was like a ritual for him. Prostitutes, strip clubs, violent pornography. Olivia told me he used to go to this brothel in Reno and pay money to tie women up and sodomize them.

GLADSTONE: For a man of his size, Langer was a surprisingly agile thief. He liked breaking into houses and stealing things he could sell, but he also had a preference for hiding out—in closets or spare bedrooms, mostly—just to see how long he could stay in someone's house without getting caught. He called it "creepy crawling."

He'd rob a house, stealing things that people wouldn't notice were missing right away, and then wait for them to go to bed. He'd watch them sleep, or see how close he could get to their bed without them waking up. It was really bizarre and scary.

But Langer never attacked the people in the houses he stole from. He saved that for the girls he picked up, for the men he met at bars and nightclubs—and especially for Olivia Lucero. It was a special kind of rage he had—the kind he could only deliver with his bare fists.

When he couldn't tie Coral Harrington up, when she resisted him, he felt that rage. You can blame it on a lot of factors—his abusive childhood, his addiction to pornography—whatever. But a killer walked to the back of the cabin that night, and he found Coral, and he did unspeakable things to her.

(REENACTMENT): *Coral Harrington, dressed in a tank top and sweatpants, listens from the door of the cabin's back bedroom.*

From the kitchen she hears crashing, screaming, limbs in violent motion. Panicked, she rushes to the bedside table, grabs her cell phone, and tries to dial 911—but there's no reception.

She darts to the sliding glass door at the back of the room, hurls it open, frantically punching buttons on the phone—and runs straight into Clive Langer, his mask-ringed eyes burning like two black coals.

Coral screams, stumbles backward, and drops the phone.

Langer crushes the phone with his boot. He whips the rope from his belt and grins, showing a row of decaying teeth through the mask's cracked-open mouth.

Coral lunges for the sliding glass door, attempting to pull it closed...

(NARRATIVE FOOTAGE)

In the present day, CHERIE ALVAREZ, now 19, sits on the porch swing outside her childhood home in Gilroy, California.

ALVAREZ: In the hospital I had dreams about Coral. She was smiling and happy. But then I'd wake up. And in those first few seconds of being awake, I would believe she was really alive—and then reality would settle in, the terror and the evil of that night, and I'd start to cry.

Coral was my best friend. She loved bubblegum ice cream. Sometimes she would laugh so hard that she would start to hiccup. She could recite "The Raven" by heart and knew when to look in the sky for certain stars. She was always there for me. But when she needed my protection, I failed. The phone line in the cabin was dead. I couldn't get reception on my phone. I couldn't call anyone for her. I couldn't help.

That's how I ended up at Centered Health for two months after the killings, trying to get over the guilt. Trying to forget and remember at the same time. My doctor said it wasn't my fault, but I never believed him.

Coral and Paula looked out for their friends. They accepted people for their differences. Paula was an amazing dancer, and Coral wrote these incredible stories and plays. Other than my father, they were the two people I loved and trusted the most in the world.

KATIE MORRISON *is an adjunct drama and writing professor at San Jose State University. A stage director and advisor for the school's literary magazine, she is 44.* Coral didn't mince words with her writing. Even though she was a fan of writers like Poe and M.R. James, her style was more threadbare and lean. Our school's literary magazine published two of Coral's stories. One of them was a sort of epistolary dossier about a haunted village in Britain. I loved it. Her stories were very modern but with a Gothic sensibility.

When I heard about Coral's murder, my first thought was that she had been killed by a real-life monster. Her death has left a hole in my heart—for me and the entire school.

(REENACTMENT): *Inside the cabin, Coral slams the glass door on Langer's dirt-grimed fingers. Undeterred, he shatters the door with a ferocious kick.*

Langer steps into the room, whipping the coil of rope across Coral's face. She falls to the floor, crying out, blood seeping from her cheek.

Now on all fours, Coral begins crawling through shards of broken glass, trying to get away.

Langer snatches one of her arms and yanks it behind her back. The elbow snaps. Coral screams.

Langer kneels and tries to tie Coral's hands behind her back, but she resists, kicking and thrashing. With her good arm she grabs a shard of glass, the jagged edges digging into her palm, and slashes blindly behind her.

The first swipe—Langer dodges it.

The second swipe—the glass cuts across his undershirt and draws a line of blood. Wild-eyed and salivating, Langer utters a sound like gargled laughter.

But the third swipe catches Langer's eye, rupturing the globe and sending a stream of blood and fluid through the eye-hole of his mask. Hurling the mask from his face, he roars in pain.

Coral scrambles to the door. Half-blind, Langer grabs her foot and violently twists the ankle with both hands, snapping the tender bone.

He then drags Coral through the broken glass and starts punching her in the back. With each slamming thud Coral's spine begins to crack...

CUT TO:

(REENACTMENT CONT.): *Cherie inches her way down the hallway to the back bedroom, holding the chopping knife in front of her.*

Inside the bedroom, Langer lands blow after blow on Coral's back, his fists pounding flesh and bone. His hands covered in blood, he then takes an antique tractor grill from the wall and smashes it down onto Coral's skull just as...

...the bedroom door swings open and Cherie storms in, her knife poised for slaughter.

She stabs the blade into Langer's left ear, driving it deep, using both hands to push the handle. She then lets go, leaving the knife jammed inside his head.

Screeching like a stabbed animal, Langer falls onto the floor, grappling for the knife in his skull. He can't get a hold of it—his hands too slippery with blood.

Shocked by the sight of Coral's body, Cherie runs for the open patio.

But abruptly she stops. Hesitates.

Then returns to the room, sidesteps Langer, and begins searching through Coral's duffel bag.

Langer slides the knife out of his ear. Blood spurts from the wound, dotting the carpet in thick drops. Langer stands up, knife in hand, the blade drooling with gore.

Cherie finds what she was looking for: Coral's keychain with the pointed self-defense knuckles.

Langer charges at Cherie, his hands swinging through the air like bear paws. He punches her in the face, dropping her to one knee. Out of breath, he looms over her...

Feral now, Cherie reaches up and drives the sharp aluminum points three times into his fat belly. On the third strike, she keeps the weapon embedded as far as it can go, wiggling the blades hard and deep into Langer's guts.

Langer staggers, dropping the knife. Cherie throws down the keychain, picks up the knife, and tries to stab him.

Langer raises his hands to protect himself, and the blade drives through his palm and out the other side of his hand. Wailing, he falls to his knees.

With all her might, Cherie kicks Langer twice in the chest. The second kick spills him onto his back. His hand with the knife sticking through it comes dangerously close to stabbing his face.

Before Langer can move, Cherie is there, pushing down on his injured hand like a plunger. Grunting, she puts all her weight into it.

The knife teases the tender flesh of Langer's cheek before sinking into his face. Cherie keeps twisting and thrusting the blade, cutting through cartilage. As if having a seizure, Langer writhes on the floor.

Then, in agile motion, Cherie removes the knife from Langer's face and slashes his throat. As blood flows from the wound, Cherie rises to her feet. Looking at Coral's broken body, she lets out a choked sob.

A sharp puncturing sound from outside returns her to reality. Blinking away tears, Cherie runs to the front room and finds Paula's car keys among the couch cushions.

(NARRATIVE FOOTAGE)

DOMINICO ZAPPULA, *58, served as Bobby Pruitt's probation officer in 1994. At the age of 16, Pruitt was charged with the attempted murder of his mother's girlfriend and spent time in a juvenile detention facility.* When he was a juvenile, Bobby Pruitt stabbed a woman with a paint scraper. A few cuts closer to the jugular and she would have died. But Bobby got a judge who saw something tragic and misunderstood in the boy. The judge thought he was capable of change. And that's where I came in. My goal in working with Bobby was his rehabilitation. Juvenile detention had not been good to him. He had a drug problem. He was depressed. But I helped him get a job working in construction. I tried to get him help as far as drugs and alcohol were concerned. But what made him the happiest was Tiffany Cobb. In Bobby's eyes, she was nothing short of Mary Magdalene. And I think they loved each other very much.

LORRAINE MORGAN, *40, is Bobby Pruitt's ex-girlfriend and the owner of Lucky Duck Thrift Shop in Marietta, Ohio. She has several keepsakes from their relationship, including love letters and poems.* "Dear Lorraine—I can't always put into words the way I feel about you. But I see your smile. I hear your heartbeat. I want to be with you as I write this. I want to take away your pain."

Not a lot of people are going to believe Bobby would write something like that. I don't believe it myself—not when I see the pictures of those poor girls on the news. It was a long time ago. We were just kids, and we met at a rough time in Bobby's life. He was 18, and he and Tiffany had gotten in a fight and split up. I met him at a bowling alley and we started dating. I fell in love with him fast, the way you do when you're young, but looking back on it now, I know his heart was with Tiffany. Bobby always said they were meant for each other.

(ARCHIVED FOOTAGE): *Videotaped footage of plastic skeletons, carved pumpkins, and roaming trick-or-treaters.*

MORGAN: Halloween was our favorite time of year. We went to all the haunted attractions in our area, but Bobby had different ideas about what scared people. He saw beauty and glamour in things that most of us would consider ugly. We had a few good months together. But as time went on, Bobby started to objectify me. One night he videotaped us having sex without my knowledge. And he tied me up a few times, even though I didn't like it. I realized I was just doing whatever Bobby wanted. It was easier to keep him happy than risk making him angry.

Eventually, Bobby went back to Tiffany. At the time they were both still living in Ohio. Tiffany was a thin, nervous little wreck. I felt sorry for her. She wanted to be a photographer, but she could never get her shit together. She had a terrible diet—Twinkies, pork rinds—and she drank a lot. She had this terrible acne all over her face and back—these huge cysts and pustules that always looked infected.

Bobby got in trouble a few more times with the law—disorderly conduct, drunk in public—that sort of thing. And then years later I heard he moved to California with Tiffany.

SHELDON: Bobby and Tiffany moved to Los Angeles in 2014. It was there that Tiffany took on a more prominent role in his haunted houses and creative projects. She appeared in "Death Rituals," gutter-drunk, crawling on people naked, smearing fake blood and bodily fluids on them. It was gross and exploitative, but Bobby saw something symbolic and almost regal in her performances.

Of course, Cherie Alvarez didn't see it that way. She wrote about "Death Rituals" for a school paper, which then got picked up by the underground news and horror community. The paper got passed around on social media and people were shocked by what they read. They began to boycott "Death Rituals," and Bobby started getting a lot of negative press and hate mail. People started threatening him and Tiffany online. And as retaliation to his critics, he jumped into his next project quickly. But he didn't have the necessary precautions in place, and that led to the tragedy in the desert.

(ARCHIVED FOOTAGE)

NEWS REPORTER, *inside the KCRA newsroom.* An event promising participants the opportunity to live out their own survival horror movie has concluded with a gruesome discovery today in the Indio Desert. Police have identified the mutilated body of 37-year-old Tiffany Cobb, an exotic dancer who had been working at an event called "Personal Demons," a role-playing simulation created by her boyfriend, a controversial figure in the world of Halloween entertainment. Investigators say Cobb was the victim of a violent physical assault that resulted in her death. At this time, the suspect or suspects in the case remain at large…

JOE MARTINEZ, *a 15-year veteran of the Indio Police Department and currently investigating the murder of Tiffany Cobb. He is 48.* She was kicked in the head repeatedly with a pointed-toe boot, which fractured her skull and caused bleeding in her brain. We found foot and heel marks on the victim's face and torso, which indicated that she had been viciously stomped on.

MORGAN: Bobby once told me that when one of them died, the other would surely die after. That's the kind of relationship he had with Tiffany.

MARTINEZ: Law enforcement is still actively seeking Tiffany's killer. But it's an open case, so there's not much else I can say about it at this time.

(NARRATIVE FOOTAGE)

MEDIUM SHOTS of Los Feliz, the East Los Angeles neighborhood where Bobby Pruitt and Tiffany Cobb were renting an apartment in 2016.

STUART GILMAN, *a homicide detective for the Los Angeles Police Department for the past 6 years. He is 41-years-old.* Communicating with El Dorado County police, we searched the residences of the three attackers at Apple Hill. Pruitt's apartment turned up some interesting finds. He collected books about suicide and death. Nietzsche's *Will to Power*. Swedenborg's *Heaven and Hell*. We found ammunition for a .32 caliber handgun and surveillance photographs of Cherie Alvarez. But it was in Pruitt's private journals where we learned how much the assault on Tiffany impacted him. I'll read a passage here:

"Today I identified her body. Someone kicked her face in and dislocated her jaw. They gouged out one of her eyes and cut up her body with a knife. They choked her with pages from the Bible...

"With all kindness and forgiveness gone in the world, there is nothing to do but create and destroy—the work and the self."

Then, just a few pages later, his sadness turns to anger and the desire for revenge.

"Rage, grief, the need to blame someone, anyone, sometimes to the point of obsession, even homicidal fantasy."

GLADSTONE: In the lead-up to the crimes at Apple Hill, Pruitt had turned manic, even suicidal. His latest haunted attraction had led to the death of his girlfriend, and he felt tremendous guilt about that. The event failed commercially. People who attended were threatening lawsuits. Meanwhile, he was growing obsessed with Cherie Alvarez. He thought she was the catalyst to all his problems. He began sending Moore and Langer on trips to Northern California to spy on Cherie and gather information. There, they stole her planner and pocketbook.

When he learned about the vacation in Apple Hill, Pruitt saw an opportunity. He was a desperate, bitter man, but he was also a coward. You see, Pruitt was the only one to not bring a mask to the cabin. He never had any intention of going inside that house. Instead, he got two stupid ex-cons to do his dirty work for him.

(OVER CRIME SCENE PHOTOS)

Paula Green was dead in the kitchen, her left knee broken, her throat slashed. Colin Moore was on the floor next to her, stabbed in the chest and neck. The bodies of Coral Harrington and Clive Langer were in the back bedroom. Coral had been beaten to death. Langer's throat was cut, his left artery severed.

There was blood everywhere in the cabin—on the floors and carpet. On the kitchen cabinets. The clothes on the victims were soaked in blood. One of the more telling pieces of evidence were the bloody footprints going to and from the cabin. Those belonged to Cherie Alvarez. We were able to follow her footsteps right to her confrontation with Bobby Pruitt.

ALVAREZ: I had Paula's keys and my phone. My only thought at that point was to get to the car and drive to where I could get reception and call 911. I thought it was over. I didn't think there were any more people in the cabin. But I was in a fog. My body felt numb. I walked out the front door. I walked to the jeep with the phone in my hand. I remember looking at the blood on my hands and feet and thinking, "This has happened before." It was this terrifying feeling of déjà vu.

(ARCHIVED FOOTAGE): *From various news agencies and "live" reports.*

UNIDENTIFIED MALE REPORTER: A shocking story out of Gilroy, California tonight—a home invasion leaves a pregnant mother hammered to death and her young daughter trembling in fear and horror in a bedroom closet...

UNIDENTIFIED FEMALE REPORTER: An official announcement from the Gilroy Police Department indicates that the child discovered her mother's body and still had the courage to call 911...

UNIDENTIFIED FEMALE REPORTER: Police had to rely on the eyewitness testimony of a frightened 7-year-old girl, who provided investigators with the details they needed to catch their suspect, a former mental patient named Alfred Mitchell...

(NARRATIVE FOOTAGE)

BRANDON BITLER, *45, a police officer for the Gilroy Police Department in Gilroy, California. He was one of the first responders to the scene of Gloria Alvarez's murder in 2003.* I've been a police officer for over 20 years, and the Gloria Alvarez crime scene is still the worst of my career. She was only 29-years-old, and pregnant with her second child. She died a painful and violent death, as did the baby inside her.

(OVER PHOTOS OF ALVAREZ FAMILY AND MUG SHOTS OF ALFRED MITCHELL)

Mike Alvarez, Gloria's husband, encouraged the court to commit Alfred Mitchell to a mental institution for the rest of his life. In statements to the judge, he and Cherie forgave Mitchell for killing the one person they loved the most. And I think we can all learn from a gesture like that.

Inside the cabin that night, Cherie did whatever she could to survive. Moore and Langer were in the process of committing a disgusting crime, and Cherie only wanted to save herself and her friends. But when she confronted Bobby Pruitt outside, she had a choice to make. And once again, she showed the compassion and sensibility that have defined her entire life. I think Pruitt saw that compassion within her, and he hated it. He felt ashamed because of it. Ashamed because he wasn't half the person Cherie was. And I think that's why he did what he did.

MORGAN: It killed Bobby to see Tiffany suffer like that, to be beaten to death, and to know in his heart that it wasn't a research paper written by some college kid responsible for it. It was Bobby. He put her in that situation. He exploited her, parading her around at his shows, promoting violence and torture. Something like this was bound to happen. He was always a somber and brooding man, but it was that guilt-ridden state of mind he found himself in that explains his actions in the end.

(REENACTMENT): *As if sleepwalking, Cherie stumbles out into the night. She moves slowly toward Paula's jeep, the wind blowing hard against her cold face and hands.*

As she eyes the Buick parked several yards away, she fails to get reception on the cell phone.

She reaches the car, fumbles with the keys—but she then sees that the tires have been slashed, the blade of a pocketknife jutting out from one of them.

With nowhere else to go, Cherie turns toward the Buick Regal just as...

...a figure rises from behind the jeep, crossing into a narrow blade of light to reveal:

Bobby Pruitt aiming a .32 caliber handgun at Cherie. But when he sees her, her face battered and her clothes covered in blood, he looks truly shocked.

PRUITT: What the hell happened in there? What'd you do, you crazy bitch?

Cherie's eyes narrow to slits, her forearms corded tight. Her fingers curl around the car keys, turning them into a weapon.

Pruitt steps closer. He tries to steady the gun, his hand shaking, the silence grating on his nerves. The scar on his neck begins to throb, a jagged white line in the moonlight.

Cherie stands her ground, body taut as wire, ready to spring. Pruitt eyeballs her. Far off in the distance, the dog begins to bark again.

CUT TO:

(NARRATIVE FOOTAGE)

ALVAREZ: I didn't want to hurt him—but I wasn't going to back down. I told him to give me the gun. I told him he could drive us to the police station in Placerville, and I was going to keep the gun on him the whole way.

At the time I didn't recognize him. I had only seen his picture a few times. It was only later that I found out he had come for me—that he blamed me for his girlfriend's death.

(REENACTMENT – NARRATIVE FOOTAGE – CONTINUOUS)

Outside the cabin, Pruitt inches closer to Cherie. He has the gun aimed at her chest, his face slick with sweat, the neck muscles strained.

Cherie edges right, as if to flank him. She flexes her fingers around the car keys. And from the darkness, the dog's barking grows higher in pitch.

ALVAREZ: His face twisted into this ugly mask—full of hatred and anger and pain. He couldn't hold the gun straight. The moonlight caught the pale white of his eyes, and he looked out of his mind. I could tell he didn't want to shoot me. He was drifting—drifting away. For a moment it seemed like I wasn't even there—like he was looking *past* me—into some other world.

CUT TO:

(REENACTMENT – CONTINUOUS): *A cemetery in Los Angeles County. Raining and cold. A casket is lowered into the ground. A small gathering stands before a PRIEST as he finishes the eulogy.*

Bobby Pruitt stands foremost among the motley group, his dark eyes swelling with tears. A red bolo tie sharply contrasts his scruffy black suit. He steps up to the open grave. He stares down into the darkness of the hole where the coffin now rests.

Shattered, Pruitt reaches down and grabs a handful of dirt. He tosses the dirt into the grave. He steps back, stumbling, and one of the mourners has to help him up. Pruitt lashes out, sobbing, mad with grief. The rain falls in an endless, stinging torrent.

The priest finishes the eulogy. Pruitt looks blankly around the cemetery. At the crumbling tombstones. At the dying flowers. He looks up to the pouring sky— remembering.

CUT TO:

(A MEMORY FLASH)

Bobby Pruitt follows an ORDERLY down a hospital corridor. The orderly holds a clipboard.

CUT TO:

Pruitt and the orderly enter the morgue. The room is brightly-lit, white-tiled and almost blinding. In the center of the room—five autopsy tables. Against the far wall—several rows of numbered crypts. The orderly checks his paperwork, then walks to a specific crypt. Pruitt follows.

The orderly opens the door and draws out the pallet. As Pruitt watches, the orderly pulls down the sheet covering the body.

(SERIES OF SHOTS)

Tiffany's tangled hair, flecked with dried blood – her hemorrhaged eye, blood pooled between the cornea and iris – one side of her face smashed in.

(BACK TO REENACTMENT)

At Tiffany's gravesite, Pruitt suddenly lunges toward the open hole. Screaming all his love. All his hate. He wants to climb into the grave, into the coffin, with Tiffany. The mourners hold him back. The rain slashes down. Pruitt drops to his knees, raging against the world.

(NARRATIVE FOOTAGE – REENACTMENT – CONTINUOUS)

ALVAREZ: He got closer to me, the gun held loosely in his hand. So close I could smell the cigarettes on his breath. Cigarettes and alcohol.

Pruitt and Cherie circle each other like starving vultures, but Pruitt can't keep the gun steady. The seconds pound down like thunder...

ALVAREZ: In his face I recognized something—at the time I wouldn't have been able to describe it. But the image is more firmly planted in my mind now. It was the totality of his misery. Of everything he had done—and all that he had lost. Without saying a word, he put the gun to his head and pulled the trigger.

A deafening shot. Pruitt is blown out of the frame as blood sprays onto the window and door of the jeep.

Cherie screams.

CUT TO BLACK:

(REENACTMENT MONTAGE)

From a muggy morning in the Sierra Nevada mountains, clouds scudding across the sky.

To Bobby Pruitt, a single bullet hole in the side of his head, his body slumped against the jeep.

To Paula Green's body on the kitchen floor of the cabin, throat slashed, her mouth rimmed with blood.

To Colin Moore's body, the metal skewer sticking out of his neck.

To several police cruisers roaring down the mountain highway, sirens flashing.

Down the cabin hallway, the floor covered in bloody footprints.

To the bedroom, where Coral Harrington's body lies soaked in gore, her mouth stretched wide in a silent scream.

To Clive Langer's body nearby, a gaping slash across his neck, his hand pinned to his mangled face with the chopping knife.

To police officers entering the cabin, moving down the hallway, clearing the rooms. To a closet in the back bedroom, a police officer carefully opening the door. It swings open, the officer pulls his gun...

Cherie curled in a fetal position inside the closet. Her face bruised and smeared with blood, her eyes scrunched shut. She has an open wound on the left side of her head, with clotted blood caked on her left temple.

BLOND POLICE OFFICER, *staring in amazement*: We need an ambulance here right away. Jesus Christ.

BROWN-HAIRED POLICE OFFICER: Is she alive?

BLOND POLICE OFFICER, *his voice fading, as if in a dream*: Ma'am, are you all right? Can you hear me? I need you to open your eyes. Can you do that for me?

Cherie remains still, her eyes fluttering from behind their lids.

BLOND POLICE OFFICER, *fading to silence*: That's it, just like that...open your eyes...

Cherie groans. Blood trickles from her mouth. She opens her eyes.

(NARRATIVE FOOTAGE)

J. GREEN: Night after night, with every news report and TV special, my family has had to relive the horror of what happened inside our cabin that night. It's been heartbreaking to watch.

GLADSTONE: The killings have affected all of El Dorado County. The towns have changed. The people have changed. One of the reasons my department agreed to this film was so that we could stop reliving this case in the media. To tell the truth of what happened, to make sure Cherie is getting the help she needs, to put this tragedy behind us and try to heal.

(ARCHIVED FOOTAGE): *A return to* THE NATIONAL DISH *Newsroom and the Busty Female Reporter.*

BUSTY FEMALE REPORTER: The rumor mill is spinning wildly out of control now that Cherie Alvarez has returned home after spending two months in a recovery center for young adults—a place sources say is nothing more than a dumping ground for people with severe psychological disorders.

Two months since Cherie mutilated and killed the thugs who broke into her friend's cabin, leaving their bodies in pieces.

Two months since Bobby Pruitt committed grisly suicide after confronting Cherie outside the residence.

Two months since Cherie entered a psych ward after suffering from post-traumatic stress and began taking anti-psychotic drugs.

The National Dish is the only news agency brave enough to ask the tough questions. Here are just a few...

According to her written statement to the El Dorado County police, Cherie had the chance to flee the cabin once she knew her friends were dead. She could have run away. She could have flagged down a car and gotten help. Instead, she searched for a weapon and used it to stab one of the attackers in the stomach before cutting his throat...

Despite the media frenzy surrounding the case and Cherie's contractual agreement with Spark TV to participate in a televised version of the events, the El Dorado County Sheriff's Office has been oddly quiet about the slayings, providing carefully scripted answers to questions about Bobby Pruitt's alleged suicide.

What was the shape of the gunshot wound on the side of Bobby Pruitt's head? What was the angle of the shot? Was it consistent with a suicide? The cops won't say.

Was there gunpowder residue on Pruitt's shooting hand? Sheriff Doug Gladstone says yes. But the public has yet to see a single photograph or legal document indicating this is true.

What was the distance of the gun from Pruitt's body at the time of the shooting? No comment, according to every investigating officer we spoke to.

The specter of murder and death has haunted every fictional story Cherie Alvarez ever wrote. Was her explanation of Bobby Pruitt's death just another convenient slice of fiction, too?

How does Cherie account for the blunt force trauma on the top of her head? Her detailed description of her fight with Moore and Langer doesn't include any indication of such an injury. And what kind of weapon made the wound?

Could it have been the butt of Bobby Pruitt's gun?

And if an ensuing struggle followed, could Cherie have gained control of that gun and executed Pruitt with a single shot? If so, why not tell the truth? Why is she lying?

As the case becomes fodder for books and made-for-television movies, will Cherie Alvarez's claims be viewed with admiration or with increasing skepticism? To find out, keep your eyes glued to *The National Dish* print edition, website, and Twitter feed...

(NARRATIVE FOOTAGE)

GLADSTONE: We stand by our investigation. However amateur they might have been, those men went to the cabin with the intent to do harm to three innocent people. They brought rope, zip-ties, a hammer, and a gag. One of them brought a gun and fortunately turned the weapon on himself before he could hurt anyone.

Police found Cherie huddled in a closet, covered in blood. She didn't orchestrate this event. She didn't plan it. She was traumatized by it. We found her fingerprints on the knife and the metal skewer. We did not find her prints on the gun belonging to Bobby Pruitt. We did find gunshot residue on Cherie's hands, but that could have come from anywhere, including Bobby Pruitt or our own officers who tended to Cherie before the ambulance arrived. Based on the evidence, we determined it was an instance of cross-contamination and nothing more.

The world is not a safe place. It's not a moral or ethical place. Bad things happen to good people. But that's no reason to cast blame where none is warranted.

J. GREEN: I admired my sister for her strength and courage to live her life the way she wanted to—to pursue a career in the arts. It's not easy to become a professional dancer or actress. It takes years of dedication and training, but Paula was always willing to put in the time and the work. She overcame a lot—a learning disability when she was a kid and some personal difficulties in her teen years. She was such a fighter. I loved her with all my heart.

MORRISON: The method of Coral's death was especially cruel, and it's even worse when I think about what she would have contributed to this world if she had lived.

ALVAREZ: I don't want to think about those men anymore. I don't want to think about how they came into Paula's home and violated it. But at that point, in the cabin, what mattered? I was marked. Jinxed. Cursed by death. That's how I felt. So when people ask how I could do what I did, I tell them it was worth the risk of being killed because I wasn't sure if my life was worth living.

Why I didn't run when I had the chance? I don't know—it all happened so fast. One reporter said that I "responded like a wild dog," and I guess that's true. But I was sick of being dumped on. Sick of being pushed around. I thought about my father, and all he had been through. I thought about my mother. And I thought about the truth behind my mother's death.

I've never made this statement publicly before. It's something only my father and the Gilroy police know. But when I was child, I saw my mother being killed. Nobody knows that. We never told the press. They all thought I was hiding in a closet in the back of the house, but that's not true.

I saw Alfred Mitchell raise a hammer above his head and smash it down onto her head—six, maybe seven times—smiling and laughing as he did it.

I heard my mother scream. I heard her call my name. I saw her hands instinctively protect her womb and the baby inside her, which allowed Mitchell to use the hammer on her face without any obstruction. And Mitchell used that hammer. He used it with equal amounts of joy and rage.

And I saw my mother's blood, the blood that had given me life, splashed on the walls and floor. Mitchell danced around in her blood. He rubbed it onto his mask and clothes. He put his fingers into his mouth and sucked the blood from his gloves. I saw him do this.

And I was too scared to save her. I was too small. All I could do was run to the bedroom closet and hide. It was only later, after I heard Mitchell leave the house, that I came out of the closet and called 911. I was a scared little girl. I didn't know what else to do.

But I'm not scared anymore. I'm not a little kid. And I'm a lot stronger than people give me credit for.

Inside the cabin that night, I knew that no matter what I did, my dad would always love me. I could fight back—I could become a killer—and my father would never turn his back on me. We had been through hell, and I knew we deserved more from life. So I decided I would live. I wasn't going to let Langer desecrate Coral's body. I wasn't going to let him kill me. I would survive. I would keep the life that was rightfully mine and return to my father's home where I grew up. And I did.

I don't know why Bobby Pruitt shot himself. He was either going to kill me and go to prison for the rest of his life, or he was going to die. Maybe he had a death wish. Maybe seeing me made him realize how bad things had gotten. How stupid and thoughtless his plans were, how pointless it was to come after me. Or that by killing himself, he could be reunited with Tiffany. I don't know. But I didn't kill him. You can say what you want about me. That I'm a liar. That I was driven to the brink of madness. That I'm crazy, a cold-blooded psychopath. Say what you want, but I didn't kill him.

(ARCHIVED FOOTAGE): *Outside the Apple Hill cabin at dusk. Quiet. The sun falling behind the mountain range. The forest darkens.*

The star-shaped Christmas lights blink on and off from the roof of the cabin. The weathervane creaks in the wind.

And a dog barks from deep in the woods.

"Against All Odds: Catching Up with Cherie Alvarez" by Cecelia Armstrong (originally published in *The Gilroy Press* Online Edition, October, 2017):

It's been a little over a year since Cherie Alvarez, 20, survived a night of carnage in the woods and participated in a controversial television drama that documented her experiences.

On the coffee table in her father's living room, she has spread out a stack of college brochures and shares her excitement about returning to school in the fall.

"I might go back to San Jose State, but I'm looking at other colleges, too," Cherie says. "I want to explore what's out there. I want a change of scenery."

Cherie's life today is about education, therapy, and quality time with her family. She has started writing a memoir about her troubled past, including a chapter about her mother's murder in 2003, and plans on taking philosophy classes when she gets back to school.

So, in some ways, Cherie is like any other college student, navigating her educational path and making new discoveries about herself along the way. And yet she is markedly different from others her age. She still bears the physical and emotional scars of that tragic night in the mountains, when three criminals broke into a vacation home and committed horrendous acts of violence that left two of her friends dead and Cherie severely injured.

Now, Cherie hopes she can show other victims of violence that survival is possible, and that through various cathartic methods they can rediscover peace and happiness.

For Cherie, one of these paths to healing was to appear in *The Apple Hill Murders*, the televised docudrama that broke a cable-ratings network and garnered a broad spectrum of interpretation and criticism in the press and online.

While many audiences and media outlets praised the film and applauded Cherie's courage in the face of shocking adversity, others were left deeply disturbed by the program's unbridled depiction of violence and its exploitation of the real-life victims in the tragedy.

"Crude, bloody, and sleazy," wrote one online reviewer of the TV movie. Commented another: "A scripted cash-grab featuring a disturbed young woman who brought much of the bloodshed upon herself."

Cherie was surprised to discover that some of the online comments referred to her years of being bullied in school and her interest in dark literature and film.

"People knew about my past, and they used that to color me in a certain light," says Cherie. "But my decisions that night were based on my survival. On my desire to live. That's all I can really say."

Cherie shared another reason for her participation in the docudrama: she felt it was something her mother, who was pregnant with her second child at the time of her death, would have wanted her to do.

"My mom never had a voice in the crime committed against her. She never had the chance to fight back, and I never had a chance to save her," Cherie says. "That's what the TV movie was about. It was a testament to me and Coral and Paula, and to their memory, and it didn't shy away from the horror of what we went through."

Cherie had declined to be a part of previous efforts to tell her story, including a televised special proposed by entertainment news affiliate *The National Dish*. But when Spark TV contacted her and explained its theatrical but honest approach, Cherie began to consider the possibility. In addition to talking to her doctor, she had lengthy discussions with her father and their lawyer about the project.

"I was just out of the hospital and still undergoing a lot of emotional recovery. I felt guilty about certain things and unsure of myself," she says. "But Paula's family had agreed to be in it, and [producer] Brant Kulchner has a strong background in reality-procedurals," Cherie says. "He and I wanted to tell the truth about what happened that night."

Many of the participants in *The Apple Hill Murders* met during the course of filming, making sure that they felt well-represented and that their words were not spun out of context. Cherie was able to reunite with one of her former professors at San Jose State and had the opportunity to thank the police officers who had arrived at the scene and ushered her to safety.

"My father stayed with me during all of the interviews, and the entire production team was really nice to us," Cherie says. "They understood the pain of our memories and treated us with respect."

Although Cherie wants to focus on her education and rebuild her life, she is aware of her perception in the media. She understands that the TV movie revealed certain discrepancies in her narrative, and she knows that there are people who believe she used excessive force when defending herself against her attackers.

"My doctor said I had what's known as dissociative fugue, a kind of temporary amnesia. As a result, the reenactments in the show were not supposed to be viewed like a documentary," she explains carefully. "Those parts were a dramatic portrayal of the events as best as I could remember them and as the evidence at the crime scene revealed."

When asked to respond to the extreme acts of violence that she witnessed and committed at the mountain cabin, Cherie can only shake her head, the memories still too raw and disturbing to digest.

"In my memoir, I'm not going to describe in detail what happened in Paula's cabin," Cherie stresses now. "Those men don't deserve any more of a legacy than they already have."

Though it has proven difficult, Cherie has also kept up with the recent events surrounding her mother's killer, Alfred Mitchell, who currently resides in a state hospital in California.

"It's been 14 years [since the murder], and there's now talk of him being conditionally released into the community," she says. "I know the prosecutors in the original case are against it, but I have to just keep moving forward and stay positive."

For years, the case against Alfred Mitchell, 50, had been mired in extensive court hearings over his legal competency. Ultimately, he was sentenced to life in a state mental hospital in 2005. However, a psychiatric evaluation in 2016 found that Mitchell had improved and was ready for conditional release under strict supervision.

"Maybe he's changed, but I'm still the same person I always was. I have the ability to forgive. I'm just much more guarded now," Cherie says. "I have to trust that the legal system won't allow him to victimize anyone else."

Mike Alvarez says that his daughter is making a slow but steady transition back into her normal life and facing the grim realities of the past. They spend a lot of time talking about the healing process and the anxiety and depression that often stem from experiencing trauma.

"She's learning to not always be in danger mode, thinking that a threat is lurking around every corner," Mr. Alvarez says. "Her survival instinct is still on high alert. She gets angry sometimes, she has a temper, but she goes on long walks and drives to Salinas to cool down."

Cherie Alvarez says that she has enjoyed going to counseling, meeting other trauma survivors, and learning how to overcome the guilt she feels about that terrible night in Apple Hill.

"It's empowering to learn that what you're feeling is okay, that you have a right to live as much as anyone else and that your actions are justified," she says. "I feel stronger and more determined now than ever before."

COMMENTS:

Amber Lee
5 hours ago

I don't buy it. She's trying to come across as this holier-than-thou figure while actively choosing not to deal with her own shit. Granted, she never asked to be famous, but if things went down in the cabin the way she described, there's no way that she could remain so level-headed, at least not so soon. There's more to this story than we know. The girl's a ticking time bomb.

Psych101
4 hours ago

I can't believe they're letting Alfred Mitchell out. The SOB fooled them all.

Flowerchild1990
4 hours ago

Amber Lee, you are clearly harboring some deep-rooted pain by attacking others who have their own way of healing from trauma. I have no doubt that Cherie is putting up a bit of a front, but to say that she's a "ticking time bomb" is to deny a young woman her chance at a decent future.

AthenaWarrior
3 hours and 45 min ago

Something's wonky about this case. Did anyone notice how many times the word "guilt" comes up in this article? I'm not sure what to believe about that. There were no other witnesses in the cabin that night to support Cherie's claims. All we have is her word and the word of the investigating officers, none of whom came off as very convincing in the movie.

Jackson
3 hours and 30 min ago

A young woman, barely in her 20s, trying to find a positive aspect to her ordeal, and yet you all feel qualified to condemn how she handles her grief and pain. There were dead bodies and blood everywhere and yet this is what you choose to whine and gossip about. Pruitt, Langer, and Moore are the real villains here. And Pruitt was such a coward that he killed himself. May they all rot in hell.

IgnorantCrimes
3 hours and 25 min ago

Ah, Jackson, the magic of ultra-sensationalized TV. Of course Bobby Pruitt blew his brains out. He was a lovesick goon with nothing else to live for. Give me a break.

DavidY
3 hours ago

We will never truly know everything that happened that night. Cherie even says that in her memoir she's not going to tell the whole story. But it's wrong to blame her. No matter what Cherie has to feel guilty about, she's still a victim and no one should judge her.

AthenaWarrior
3 hours ago

DavidY, there's a lot that this article leaves out. Sometime that night, Cherie took a blow to the top left side of her head. The police found her huddled in a closet. She was terrified, shaking all over. And yet to this day she has not been able to provide a reason for that injury, a fact that the TV movie conveniently overlooked.

DavidY
2 hours and 50 min ago

She was hit across the head with a hammer and punched in the face. Ricky Sheldon's book says that's how she got the head wound.

AthenaWarrior
2 hours and 30 min ago

The hammer nearly dislocated her jaw. Clive Langer split her lip and dislodged two of her front teeth. I'm talking about the wound on the top of her head on the left side. The one that covered her face in blood. Ricky Sheldon, hack writer extraordinaire, doesn't know jack about this case and neither do you.

FlowerChild1990
2 hours ago

Unless you're one of the police officers in charge of the investigation, AthenaWarrior, why do you care?

AthenaWarrior
2 hours ago

I care because she said she feels guilty, and I'm wondering what exactly she's feeling guilty about. Feeling guilt implies you've done something wrong.

DavidY
1 hour and 45 min ago

No! Cherie feels guilty because she did what she could to save her friends and they still died! Get a clue!

Christine
1 hour and 30 min ago

I have to chime in on this. The El Dorado County Sheriff's Office has failed to provide substantial evidence to support that Bobby Pruitt committed suicide. It's been suggested more than once that the wound on Cherie's head came from the butt of his gun. There was a tussle of some kind, and she grabbed the gun and blew his head off. Hey, the dude was as scuzzy as they come, but Cherie Alvarez is guilty of murder.

DavidY
1 hour ago

Wrong on two counts, Christine. First, Cherie didn't even know it was Pruitt when she got outside. She said so in the movie. And second, if you defend yourself using deadly force and the attacker dies you have committed homicide—not murder! Let's say Cherie did shoot and kill Pruitt. California law says you are not required to run away from danger and you can even pursue your attacker if you choose. From a legal perspective, it's the job of the detectives and the district attorney to determine whether the homicide she committed is legally justified. Anyway, they didn't find her prints on the gun, so what does it matter? Case closed.

Christine
45 min ago

Case closed? Hardly. The public's perception of Cherie Alvarez is one of mistrust and fear. This is a girl who's been obsessed with violence her entire life. A girl who wrote a play about satanic worship. A girl who enjoys killing—a monster. Don't you think it's time she set the record straight?

FlowerChild1990
35 min ago

Those poor girls were treated like prey that night. Spied on. Beaten and gutted and killed. And you know what makes this even worse? The number of women out there who say, "I've been assaulted, too. Hit by my husband. Stabbed by my boyfriend. But I never had the courage to speak out because I was afraid people would think I was lying." Cherie defended herself against a gang of degenerate pigs. She massacred those fuckers and rightly so. She doesn't have to answer to you people, or anyone else.

KingJames

20 min ago

She'll have to answer to God when the time comes. "And you will receive a rich welcome into the eternal kingdom of our Lord and Savior Jesus Christ." —2 Peter 1:11

"California Mental Patient's Body Found in Salinas River" by Calvin Southgate (originally published in *The Salinas Daily*, December, 2017, p. 1-2):

Monterey County homicide detectives are investigating the death of a mental patient whose body was discovered washed up on the muddy bank of the Salinas River on Saturday morning.

In 2003, Alfred Mitchell was charged with the murder of a 29-year-old Gilroy woman who was pregnant at the time of her death. He was convicted and sentenced to life at Atascadero State Hospital in San Luis Obispo County in 2005.

Court records indicate that Mitchell was granted a conditional release from the hospital in 2017 and was allowed to reenter society under strict supervision. How the 51-year-old evaded his supervisor and reached his hometown of Salinas from the Atascadero community remains unknown.

His throat stabbed and his face severely wounded, his body washed onto a grouping of rocks on the shore of the Salinas River, directly across from the outdoor homeless camp where he once lived.

"Despite the transgressions of his past, Mr. Mitchell did not deserve to die this way," said Jack Gregory, the Monterey County sheriff. "He wasn't that old, but he had been living a fairly sedentary existence for many years. He was overweight and had developed blood clots in his leg. He might have used drugs while out of the hospital. I think his attacker took advantage of that."

Gregory said that Mitchell's body might have been in the water for as long as a week.

"His clothes were dirty and sodden, and he was found without the electronic monitoring bracelet that he was supposed to be wearing at all times," said Gregory.

Gregory added that the victim appeared to have no defensive wounds on his body, indicating that he might have been attacked by surprise, perhaps while he was sleeping or unconscious.

"We believe the victim was most likely killed at the homeless camp, probably at night, and then dumped or dragged into the water," Gregory added. "This is a very off-road location. Someone had to have gone looking for him, or known he was there."

The state department of mental health declined to discuss in detail the Mitchell case, citing privacy laws that prohibit them from talking about specific patients.

But according to a spokesperson for the department, officials followed protocol by alerting local law enforcement once they realized that Mitchell had gone missing.

The sheriff said evidence shows the victim was stabbed repeatedly with a sharp blade, most likely a pocketknife or a small lock-blade knife.

"Even something as slight as a 2-inch blade can do serious damage to the human body," Gregory said. "In the case of Alfred Mitchell, I think the knife penetrated his artery before he was even aware that he was being attacked.

"We don't have a motive at this time, but whoever did this has a lot of anger, a lot of bottled-up rage," Gregory concluded. "And my fear is that he or she won't hesitate to strike again."

The case is currently under investigation.

About The Author

Josh Hancock is a teacher and author. His first novel, *The Girls of October*, was inspired by his love of all things horror--especially John Carpenter's *Halloween*, Tobe Hooper's *The Texas Chain Saw Massacre*, and William Friedkin's *The Exorcist*. His second novel, *The Devil and My Daughter*, was equally inspired by horror films, including Amando de Ossorio's underground classic *Demon Witch Child*. For reviews, book trailers, and more, please visit www.foundfootagefiction.com.

Also by Josh Hancock:

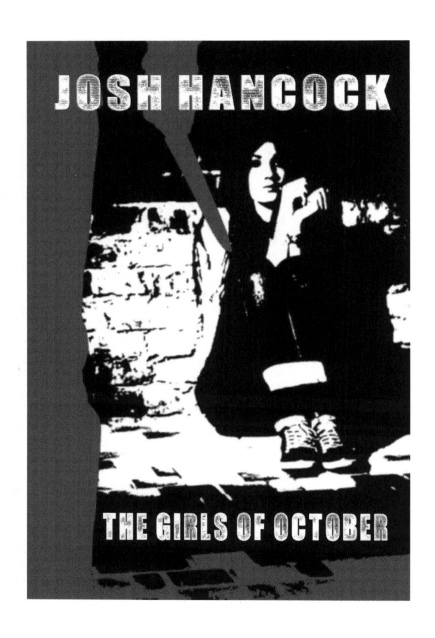

Also by Josh Hancock:

THE GIRLS OF OCTOBER

The Girls of October tells the story of a young woman who develops a strange fascination with John Carpenter's Halloween, believing that somewhere within the 1978 horror classic lays the truth behind an arcane force that has terrorized her since her childhood.

As an escape from a world that has not always been kind, film student Beverly Dreger takes comfort in spooky urban legends, horror movies, and monster magazines. But when a string of bizarre murders draws her closer to the folkloric entity known as "the bogeyman," Beverly must unravel the mystery of her past and confront an ancient evil.

An epistolary novel, The Girls of October collects fictional primary sources—newspaper articles, film criticism, screenplays, short stories, interviews, police reports, and more—to tell a chilling story of psychosis, family secrets, and murder.

Also by Josh Hancock:

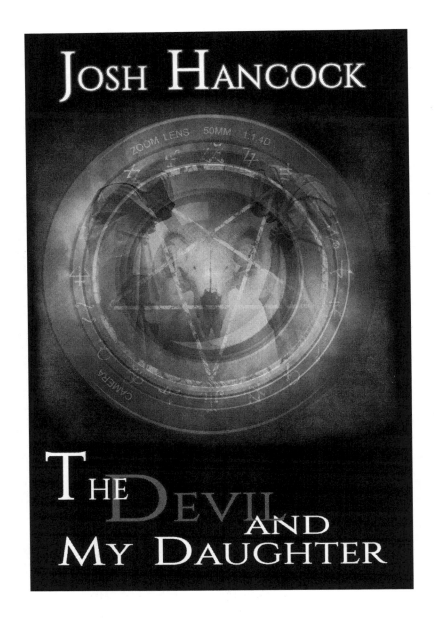

Also by Josh Hancock:

THE DEVIL AND MY DAUGHTER

1944: In the pillars of smoke that rise from the crematoriums at Auschwitz, Nazi soldiers hope to catch a glimpse of Moloch, the pagan god of child sacrifice, to whom the Third Reich owes so much of its vile success...

1977: A teenage boy writes a heavy metal song about an ancient evil spirit, unaware that the grisly lyrics will unleash a terrifying figurehead from the bowels of history...

1987: College students and best friends Debra and Charlene are determined to make a demonic possession movie more frightening than The Omen and more gruesome than The Exorcist. But when they hire a rock band to pen the film's "satanic soundtrack," the young filmmakers are confronted with a supernatural entity determined to plunge Charlene into a world of impossible terror and human sacrifice...an entity with the burning-coal eyes of a demon and the razor-sharp horns of a bull...

Written as a collection of essays, news articles, interviews, scripts, and film scholarship, *The Devil and My Daughter* tells a horrific story of the occult, Satanic possession, and ritual murder.

OTHER GREAT TITLES FROM

Burning Bulb
PUBLISHING

WWW.BURNINGBULBPUBLISHING.COM

SOON TO BE A MAJOR MOTION PICTURE!!

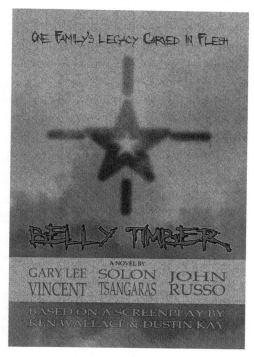

BELLY TIMBER

From the writers of Darkened Hills, Detour to Armageddon and Night of the Living Dead comes a novel unlike any other...

In the 1800's, ordinary people learned the secret of the Kala and undertook extraordinary measures to rid the earth of this evil. This is their story.

For John McCormick, life on the Indiana frontier held nothing but promise. His settlement along the White River would soon become the crossroads of America. Friends and family from back in Ohio and other points east were all making plans to see what all the fuss was about in the newly-formed city of Indianapolis. Yes, things were good. John had his general store and his friend George Pogue had his blacksmith business. Claims were being staked and relations with the native Indians were amicable. The town was growing and nothing could be better... or so he thought.

In Ohio, an evil was brewing. The Lecky Family, a group of ruthless Mongolian nomads, had made their way to America and were practicing their cannibalistic religion of Kala with reckless abandon. No one was safe, not even John McCormick's family.

Burning Bulb
PUBLISHING

GARY LEE VINCENT'S
DARKENED
THE WEST VIRGINIA VAMPIRE SERIES

DARKENED HILLS

When evil descends on a small West Virginia town, who will survive?

Jonathan did not start out his life to become a rambler, it just worked out that way. William was a troubled youth with something to hide. Both were from Melas, a small town tucked away in the West Virginia hills... a town where disappearances are happening more and more frequently.

After the suicide of a wanted serial killer, the townsfolk thought the nightmare was over. But when a centuries-old vampire is discovered they find out the hard way it's just getting started. Dark secrets can only stay hidden for so long and when the devil comes to collect, there will be hell to pay. Can Jonathan and William find a way to stop the vampire before it's too late? Find out in *Darkened Hills!*

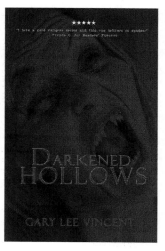

DARKENED HOLLOWS

In the heart-stopping sequel to the award-winning *Darkened Hills*, Jonathan and William must return to West Virginia to face possible criminal charges stemming from their last visit to the damned town of Melas, where both had narrowly escaped the clutches of a vampire seethe.

And as livestock start mysteriously getting murdered with all of their blood drained, worried farmers are searching for answers - leaving the local Sheriff and his deputy racing against time to learn the cause before a more violent crime is committed.

Burning Bulb
PUBLISHING

WWW.DARKENEDHILLS.COM

GARY LEE VINCENT'S
DARKENED
THE WEST VIRGINIA VAMPIRE SERIES

DARKENED WATERS

When the world goes to hell, the chosen must arise!

As Talman Cane orchestrates a flood of epic proportions in this third installment of the *Darkened* series the towns of Melas and Tarklin are caught completely off guard by the deluge. Hell-bent on finishing what they started, the evil brothers return to the lunatic asylum to take care of the witnesses and add to the ever-growing army of the undead.

Aided by Lucifer himself and the insane vampire demon Legion, the stage is set to channel all of the forces of hell to come forth. In an all-out race to survive, Jonathan, William, and Amanda soon discover they are up against impossible odds as Lucifer opens the Gateway to Hell, ushering in the zombie apocalypse and the End Times.

Find out who will survive this cosmic battle of the ages in *Darkened Waters!*

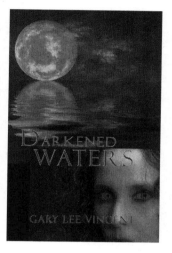

DARKENED SOULS

Melas and the Madison House are about to be rebuilt.
True evil is about to be reborne!

Young ex-priest and vampire-killer William is drawn back to the West Virginian town that almost killed him, where his vampire arch-enemy Victor Rothenstein still stalks the earth.

The town of Melas lies destroyed after the battle of the End of Days. But why is wealthy Jackie Nixon so eager to rebuild it using the bone dust of murdered souls?

Terrible evil has visited before, but the Gateway to Hell is about to be reopened in a horrific climax. And this time – it's personal.

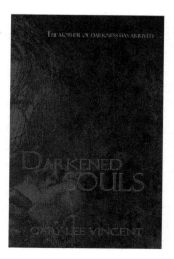

WWW.DARKENEDHILLS.COM

Burning Bulb
PUBLISHING

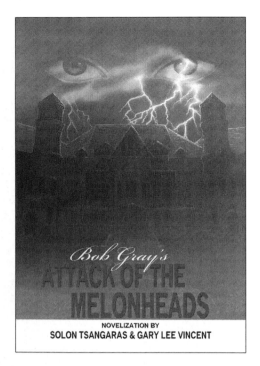

NOVELIZATION BY
SOLON TSANGARAS & GARY LEE VINCENT

BOB GRAY'S ATTACK OF THE MELONHEADS

"Melonheads is what I love. Give me a body count and gore, but don't forget the laughs. Anytime that I can be reminded of what makes Horror great it is a good thing. Melonheads does that and is something we should all support. Consider it highly recommended."
—*Screamsine.us*

Fifty years ago, a doctor sought to cure a terrible disease. Hidden from the world, Doctor Malcolm Crowe toiled in the dead of night while the world was sleeping, creating a new breed of mutant—all in the name of science.

Yes, he thought he could cure the sick children. But he was wrong.

Today, the results of his cruel and unconventional experiments have manifested into an evil never before seen.

Now, in Kirtland, Ohio, the town's unsuspecting residents are about to encounter the full onslaught of this unimaginable terror.

Can something be done before it's too late?

Burning Bulb
PUBLISHING

WOL-VRIEY
BIZARRO AND TRANSGRESSIVE FICTION

BOSTON POSH (BUD MALONE #1)

In 2028 AD, the USA is a nation ravaged by hungry dragons and dinosaurs. In Boston, Massachusetts, private eye Bud Malone is hired to rescue a kidnapped heiress. But nothing is as it seems.

Malone works to unravel a tangled web involving Boston Chinatown, a 200-year-old woman with a 9-year-old body, white robots, a human-liver-eating psychopath, a golem, a porcelain dragon, and a snake goddess with a crush on him. There's also a woman obsessed with chicken sex. Then Malone meets Posh Lane, a gorgeous call girl who's desperate to quit her pimp.

Romantic sparks ignite between Posh and Malone, but Posh's past suddenly catches up with her in a BIG way. To save Posh, Malone agrees to run a quest for Earth's new rulers, the Forks. But, Malone has no idea that agreeing to the Fork's odd request will send him on the weirdest trip he's ever been on in his life.

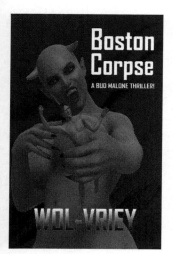

BOSTON CORPSE (BUD MALONE #2)

MAGIC CAN BE MURDER! - Drag queen Lucy Tang is back in Boston, and is hell-bent on settling her vindetta against casino owner Sookie Ling. And suddenly, Bud Malone, PI, has the case of his life to resolve.

When Boston's robot police force are baffled by a mind transfer case, they come to Malone for help. The one person who can likely help Malone out here is the witch Soledad Bathory. But Soledad seems to know a lot more than she's telling him. It's a case not made easier when Malone meets Soledad's beautiful cousin, Josephine 'Slave' Bailey. Slave has her own plans for Malone, most of which involve teaching him BDSM and making him her new Master.

Oh, and Rick Rogers owes Sookie Ling a whole lot of money, a gambling debt that's going to be literally Hell to pay!

BOSTON CORPSE - Not your average detective novel!

Burning Bulb
PUBLISHING

WOL-VRIEY
BIZARRO AND TRANSGRESSIVE FICTION

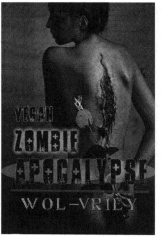

VEGAN ZOMBIE APOCALYPSE

In the post-apocalypse worlderness, zombies rule the earth. They'r allergic to meat, and brains literally make them explode. Zomb now eat blood potatoes, parasitic tubers grown in the flesh of h mancows corralled in maximum security farms. Two fugitives me in the ancient ruins of Texas. The first is Soil 15-f, a womanco who's escaped her farm a week before she's due to be killed and h blood potato crop harvested. The second fugitive is Able Kar former head necros food technician, now sentenced to death f heresy. But Soil is no ordinary humancow.

Unknown to herself, she's the vegan zombie agricultural revolutio and the zombies desperately want her back. And the necros equa desperately want Able Kane dead. He's fled with a forbidden disco ery which will reshape the world for the worse if used. And Able just hardheaded/misguided enough to use it.

MELANIE NEMESIS CATCHPOLE

In Springfield, Massachusetts, Melanie Catchpole is hired to fe back a magic teddy bear worth millions of dollars from a wareho across town. Problem is, the warehouse is down in Springfield's Zone-that totally weird sector of the city where Bizarro fell to Eart The 'O' is a fairytale land, a place where dreams and nightmares li rally live and breathe.

Worse still, the gingers—mutant cannibals—prowl the O. The ging have already eaten everyone else Melanie's employers sent to get b the magic teddy bear.

Accompanied by the handsome but ruthless Doug Fisher (who finds sexy but doesn't dare entrust her heart to), Melanie enters O-Zone. Melanie and Doug are instantly caught up in an advent they'd never have believed credible even if written as fiction . . . a Melanie's used to experiencing the very weird as the norm.

And now, additionally, there's a mystery to unravel: What does dark, freezing-cold being called The Fixer want with Mary, barkeep's daughter?

Burning Bulb
PUBLISHING

DAVID J. FAIRHEAD

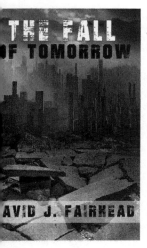

THE FALL

Hopelessness... How do you protect your loved ones when Hell itself opens its insidious mouth?

Horror... Nightmarish Creatures invade your world and there is nowhere to hide.

Blood... How long can you hold out before they come for you?

Pain... Where do you run to avoid being eaten alive by monsters with a voracious appetite for your flesh?

Screams... While you selfishly run for your own life.

Questions... Who is to blame? Where did they come from? How many people survived...and how does the human race find the means to fight back?

THE FALL OF TOMORROW is man's last tale of desperation told by those that are striving to salvage some hope against a ravenous bastion of evil beasts bent on ruling our world.

DWELLING IN THE DARK

From David J. Fairhead, author of the FALL OF TOMORROW, comes DWELLING IN THE DARK- A soulful anthology of creeping terror to keep you up in the small hours with horror set in the past, present and future. Overlapping bits of puzzle fitting each other, before and after The Fall of Tomorrow.

A place where three children facing a monstrous foe can only pray that their bloody summer would just come to an end. Go back to the 1960's- THE COMMUNE where overindulging hippies use a mage's diary to control the end of the world, only to see first-hand that their drug induced visions have horrific ramifications. Where a young boy's visit to a haunted house becomes a lesson in RESIDUAL morality. The story, DEEPER- plunges two brothers into a sinkhole only to find they were being hunted by an insidious creature from its depths. Visit the old west as hero Dekker Collins battles evil gunslingers in DEMONEYE.

And so much more...!

HELLHOLE WEST VIRGINIA

From the heights of Mothman's perch high atop the Silver Bridge in Point Pleasant to the depths of Hellhole Cavern in Pendleton County, evil lurks within the shadows as the sun sets upon the haunted hills and hollows of West Virginia.

Bizarro author Rich Bottles Jr. blows the coffin lid off horror genre clichés with this tour de force cast of Eco-friendly vampires, beach-yearning zombies and sex-starved she-devils.

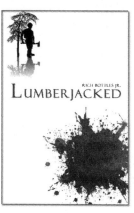

LUMBERJACKED

If you are easily offended or do not possess a truly depraved sense of humor, this story may not be the light summer reading fare you desire. As for the four feisty female freshmen stranded on top of West Virginia's third highest mountain, they have no choice but to experience the sick, twisted debauchery and perverted mayhem described deep inside the tight unbroken bindings of this horrific missive.

Lumberjacked takes the reader to a nightmarish world where character development and aesthetic integrity are prematurely cut short by the swinging axes of maniacal lumberjacks, who are hell bent on death and destruction in the remote forests of Appalachia. And at the climax, when paranoia crosses over to the paranormal, Lumberjacked makes Deliverance look like a family raft trip down the Lower Gauley.

THE MANACLED

What happens when twin brothers lease out the former West Virginia State Penitentiary with the false purpose of filming a documentary on supernatural phenomena, but their true intention is to make a pornographic movie?

Chaos ensues as the disturbed spirits of murdered convicts, along with the reanimated dead from the neighboring Indian Burial Mound, take their vengeance on the unwary and undressed trespassers.

Zombies, ghosts, mobsters and porn collide in this bizarre tale from horror author Rich Bottles Jr.

Burning Bulb
PUBLISHING

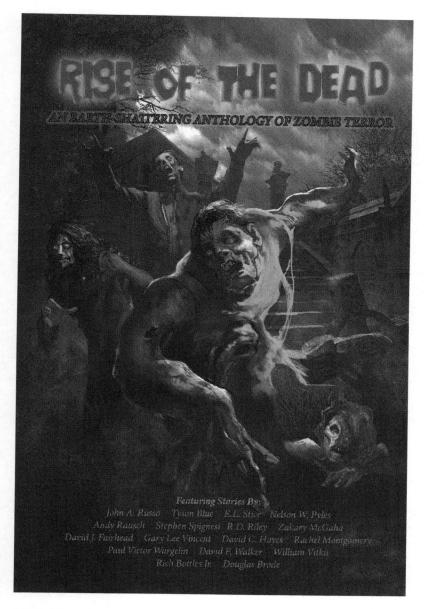

RISE OF THE DEAD - a collection of seventeen tales of unspeakable zombie terror. Featuring a foreword and short story by John A. Russo!

www.TheJohnRusso.com

Burning Bulb
PUBLISHING

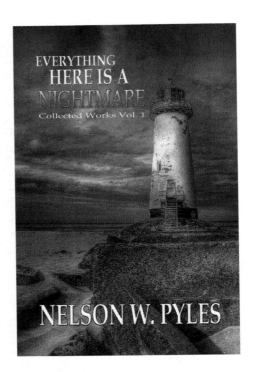

EVERYTHING HERE IS A NIGHTMARE
Collected Works Vol 1.

"Pyles makes it look easy. His characters come instantly alive with the cocksure verve and swagger of rock stars."
- Daniel Knauf, creator of HBO's "Carnivale,"
Executive Producer/Writer, ABC's "The Blacklist."

The critically acclaimed author of Demons, Dolls and Milkshakes returns with fifteen tales of horror and suspense with Everything Here is a Nightmare.

From zombies in the old west, to a young boy tempted by the Devil. From vampires with romantic longing, to an abandoned lighthouse haunted by vengeful spirits. From a serial killer getting unholy justice, to a haunted English race car, Nelson W Pyles invites you to explore a landscape of fear, suspense and horror.

Take his hand and hold on tight. Remember that whatever you find here, whatever you see, no matter what you might think it could be... know this: Everything Here is a Nightmare.

Burning Bulb
PUBLISHING

Made in the USA
San Bernardino, CA
16 September 2017